PLASTICS FILM TECHNOLOGY

PLASTICS APPLICATIONS SERIES

PLASTICS FILM TECHNOLOGY

Edited by

W. R. R. PARK

Films Research Laboratory
The Dow Chemical Company, Midland, Michigan

ROBERT E. KRIEGER PUBLISHING COMPANY
HUNTINGTON, NEW YORK
1973

Originally Published 1969
Reprint 1973

668. 414

Printed and Published by
ROBERT E. KRIEGER PUBLISHING CO., INC.
P.O. BOX 542, HUNTINGTON, N.Y. 11743

Library of Congress Catalog Card Number 73-81355
ISBN Number 0-88275-125-5

Plastics Applications Series

Allylic Resins and Monomers, *Harry Raech, Jr.*
Amino Resins, *John F. Blais*
Cellulosics, *Walter D. Paist*
Epoxy Resins, *Irving Skeist*
Gum Plastics, *M. Stafford Thompson*
Heat Sealing, *Robert D. Farkas*
High-Temperature Plastics, *Walter Brenner, Dorey Lum and Malcolm W. Riley*
Laminated Plastics (Second Edition), *D. J. Duffin*
Plastics Extrusion Technology (Second Edition), *Allan L. Griff*
Plastics Film Technology, *W. R. R. Park*
Polyamide Resins (Second Edition), *Don E. Floyd*
Polycarbonates, *William F. Christopher and Daniel W. Fox*
Polyester Resins, *John R. Lawrence*
Polyolefin Plastics, *T. O. J. Kresser*
Polystyrene, *William C. Teach and George C. Kiessling*
Polyurethanes (Second Edition), *Bernard A. Dombrow*
Polyvinyl Chloride, *Harold A. Sarvetnick*

Foreword

Plastic film development activity at The Dow Chemical Company began nearly as early as the manufacture of thermoplastic polymers and has approximately paralleled polymer developments since that time. Starting in the mid-30's, Dow began an active program on three thermoplastic materials: "Ethocel"*, ethylcellulose; saran, vinylidene chloride copolymers; and "Styron"*, polystyrene; and on one water-soluble polymer, "Methocel"*, methylcellulose.

Our first plastic film product was solvent-cast "Ethocel"*, which found utility in the packaging industry because of its good toughness, extreme optical clarity, and high surface gloss.

During World War II saran film technology was developed. It utilized a bubble technique wherein the polymer was extruded as a tube, quenched to supercool the polymer, then subsequently expanded into a trapped bubble. As the bubble expanded into the final film, crystallization took place to produce the finished film. While these principles are now well-known, at that time it was necessary to learn the precise quenching temperature needed in order to produce (in modern terminology) sufficient nuclei so that the individual crystallites would all be small and would not scatter light. Following World War II, this activity gave rise to our line of commercial saran packaging films and later to household Saran Wrap†, and finally, in the early 1960's, we started manufacture of a heat shrinkable grade of saran film.

A concurrent major plastic film development was going on with polystyrene in the 1950's. The initial purpose was to capitalize on the good dielectric properties of polystyrene film for electrical condensers and cable wrap. Over the years four different processes for producing biaxially oriented film were carried through pilot plant stage and several of them on into commercial production. These four were: the horseshoe stretcher, the bubble method, the so-called "8-sided" or pancake stretcher, and the tenter frame. "Trycite"*, a biaxially oriented polystyrene film, the culmination of these efforts, now enjoys an expanding market position. Also in the 1950's three fairly unrelated events took us heavily into polyolefin films. The first of these was the purchase of the ICI process for low density polyethylene; the second was the advent of Ziegler polyethylene for which Dow acquired a licence in 1955; and the third event was our acquisition of the Dobeckmun Company. This

---

* Registered trade names.
† Trademark of The Dow Chemical Company.

acquisition brought into Dow a wide variety of backgrounds and experiences: converted film products; lamination of films, foils, papers; various types of extrusion coatings; the manufacture of Lurex,† nontarnishable metallic yarn, and a bubble process for making polyethylene film. This latter technology eventually led to the installation of sizeable production facilities for "Polyfilm"* low density polyethylene film. Biaxially oriented polypropylene film was carried through semicommercial development, then dropped because of a change in business emphasis. A chilled roll casting process was developed for our "Handi-Wrap"* household polyethylene film. Currently, Dow is field-testing a heat-shrinkable polyolefin film of the cross-linked type.

Dow pioneered two types of water soluble films. The first was based on "Methocel."* the second on a special polyalkylene oxide.

In addition to this activity on monolithic plastic films, considerable research has been done over the years on saran barrier coatings for films. One branch of this activity developed into solvent soluble saran resins for use in the coating of cellophane and other substrates, while another branch of this activity developed into saran emulsion polymers (latexes) useful for coating polypropylene and other films.

The advent of multilayered film technology found Dow with a radically new process which had the capability of producing anywhere up to one thousand layer films using several different types of polymers with the thickness and disposition of the layers pretty much at the control of the equipment design. The "Saranex"* line of films represents our first commercialization of this concept. This material has the desirable heat seal properties of polyethylene combined with the excellent barrier properties of saran.

It is evident, from this brief synopsis, that research and development people in The Dow Chemical Company have been exposed over the last thirty years to most of the major techniques and materials for the manufacture of plastic films, and have often been the innovators in this field. In view of this diverse and varied background, it is not at all surprising that Dow personnel should be competent to engage in the preparation of the book which now follows.

R. F. BOYER

* Registered trade names.
† Trademark of The Dow Badische Company.

Preface

This book is intended to serve as a primer for technical people who work in any part of the packaging business which uses plastic films and who desire a broader knowledge of the technology. It will also give plastic technologists on overview of the utility of plastics in film form.

The contents represent a distillation of the authors' experience, opinions, and special knowledge gained through ten years of research and development activity on various plastic films, and familiarity with the rapidly expanding patent and journal literature on plastics film technology.

I am particularly indebted to J. H. Stickelmeyer, O. C. Raspor, and L. S. Mounts, all of The Dow Chemical Company, for the chapters which they contributed to the manuscript. Leon C. Stanley, of The Dow Chemical Company Audio-Visual Department, deserves special credit for the excellent job he did in preparing the illustrations.

Finally, while the opinions expressed in this book are those of the authors, we are particularly indebted to The Dow Chemical Company for encouraging this activity and for overlooking the inevitable overlap of this project into some of our working days.

Midland, Michigan
May, 15, 1969

W. R. R. PARK

Contents

Properties (seal strengths). Optical Properties (haze, gloss, transparency), Surface Properties: Blocking, Electrostatic Properties, Friction (slip), Wettability (treatment level), Miscellaneous Properties: Biological Resistance, Flatness, Odor, Orientation (shrinkage), Water Absorption, Identification of Films, Thickness Measurement, Yield (area factor).

ONE

history of plastic films

J. H. STICKELMEYER

THE PACKAGING INDUSTRY

Origins. Plastic films are a relatively recent addition to the packaging industry, which is probably as old as civilized man. The use of bags, bottles, jars, and pots for the storage and shipment of food, water, and wine in commerce dates to the early civilizations on the Mediterranean. In the commerce of the Roman Empire full use was made of then existing packaging techniques. Much of this technology was lost, and little or no progress was made during the cultural fragmentation and isolation that marked the "Dark Ages." However, the "Reawakening" of Western civilization was attended by, or perhaps even caused by, the return of cultural and commercial intercourse among states and city states. This renaissance was soon followed by the "Industrial Revolution," in which machine power and manufacturing techniques succeeded to the functions of artisans and skilled craftsmen. The emerging technology accompanied English colonists to America, in spite of attempts by colonialist powers to thwart industrialization in the colonies. Hence, the packaging industry in America may be regarded as originating in 1608, when Captain John Smith established a bottle factory at the newly formed colony at Jamestown, Virginia.

Preservation, protection, and storage of food have always been one of man's prime problems. New technology is rapidly utilized to improve methods of handling foodstuffs. Tin cans, paperboard, lead foil, and

1

paper bags were employed in food packaging almost as quickly as men could conceive of their utility in packaging, and could implement their manufacture.

FLEXIBLE PACKAGING

Paper.   The development of flexible wrapping is concomitant with the improvements in paper manufacture. Paper manufacturing in America started in 1690 in a mill established by William Rittenhouse in Germantown, Pennsylvania. More than 200 mills were in operation by 1810. The low cost manufacture of paper was facilitated by the invention of the Fourdrinier and the cylinder paper machines. The Fourdrinier, originally patented in France in 1799 by Nicholas Louis Robert, was first installed in the United States in 1827. The first cylinder type machine was installed in Wilmington, Delaware, in 1817 by Thomas Gilpin.

Severe paper shortages existed for the next fifty years because of a shortage of the raw materials then used: rags, esparto grass, and straw. Mechanical and chemical processes for converting wood pulp to papermaking pulp were invented in the mid-nineteenth century, solving the raw material problem.

Thereafter, the use of paper in packaging grew rapidly. The first paper bag machine was made in the 1860's; in 1873 a patent was issued for a satchel bottom bag. Paper's utility as an overwrap was enhanced with Gwyn's 1866 inventions for saturating paper with wax; and with Hemmersley's invention for coating paper with wax in 1877. Concurrent improvements in lithographic printing, which was developed in 1796, made possible color labeling. In 1870 boxes of chocolate candy were decorated with color lithographs of paintings, thereby introducing display packaging.

The number of paper varieties proliferated, and many specialized-use papers appeared. One pound prints of vegetable parchment were first used to wrap butter in 1888, replacing tubs. Transparency was gained through the use of wax papers; development of glassine and parchment papers gave both transparency and greaseproofness. Use of transparent wrapping and packing materials is regarded as a natural consequence of product wrapping. The open cracker barrel, cooky caddy, or bulk box display of the general store, though lacking sanitary considerations at point of sale, did offer see, touch, and taste appeal. Glass encasement of merchandise, or protective packaging in opaque materials, which sanitized food marketing, inhibited appeal to the senses.

Retail stores in the United States have evolved from general stores to specialized department stores, where goods were kept under cover for fear of pilferage and contamination, to self-service department stores and supermarkets, where goods are openly displayed and expected to sell themselves. In 1924 the demand for transparency with brilliant clarity was satisfied when duPont introduced cellophane from the first plant at Buffalo, New York. This new wrapping material was the forerunner of the plastic film industry.

PLASTICS—A BRIEF HISTORY

What are Plastics? Plastic, from the Greek word *plastikos*, was first used to imply growing, forming, or developing, especially of forces in nature. Today the term plastic is broadly applied to mean the capability of being formed and is descriptive of materials such as clay, glass, cement, putty, and asphalt. When used specifically as a noun, the word plastic describes synthetically produced materials which are capable of being shaped by heat and/or pressure in some stage of their manufacture. In general usage, cellulose derivatives are considered plastics, and cellophane is considered a plastic film.

The plastics industry owes its beginnings to the search in the nineteenth century for replacements for bone, ivory, shells, and wood, which were used for fabricating articles such as utensils, buttons, ornaments, toys, handles, and musical instruments. The first synthetic plastic, celluloid, was reported in 1865 and developed commercially in 1870 by John Hyatt, who invented a process for dissolving collodion, or pyroxylin (nitrocellulose containing 11.5–12% nitrogen), in camphor under pressure. Nitrocellulose had been first prepared in 1833 at Nancy, France by Henri Bracannot, who attempted to make films, coatings, and shapes from solutions of a product resulting from the treatment of wood and cotton with nitric acid. The utility of nitrated cellulose as a substitute for gunpowder provided the stimulus for investigations of the reaction and reaction products. Hyatt's celluloid, though first intended as a replacement for ivory in billiard balls, immediately found use in a variety of articles: combs, brush handles, dental plates, automobile side curtains, novelties, as well as the famous celluloid collar.

H. Goodwin in 1887 and H. Reichenbach in 1889 independently developed solvent casting processes for making flexible transparent nitrocellulose films for photographic uses. Processes for continuous casting were quickly developed. The success of celluloid proved the utility of plastics and sparked efforts by other workers to develop plastics which would have the virtues and none of the drawbacks of celluloid. Poor light stability, flammability, and poor solvent resistance were problems.

Cellulose remained, for a time, the main building block of investigations conducted to develop improved plastics. Schutzenberger had successfully acetylated cellulose in 1865. In 1894 the English chemists, Cross and Bevan, developed a chloroform soluble cellulose acetate. In 1903 it was discovered that highly substituted cellulose acetate, when subjected to hydrolysis, became soluble in acetone and other cheap solvents. A process for making hydrolyzed cellulose acetate commercially was developed in 1911. Its first uses were to make photographic safety film and aircraft dope. After World War I, when acetate rayon fibers and thermoplastic injection molding processes were developed, the cellulose acetate overcapacity, resulting from termination of the war effort, was almost immediately put to use. Thus was laid the groundwork for the thermoplastics industry.

TABLE 1.1.   Estimated Sales of Plastic Films* for Packaging**

| | (Millions of pounds) | | |
	1958	1962	1967
Cellophane	415	410	385
Polyethylene	183	380	775
Polypropylene	—	15	50
Polystyrene	1	7	12
"Pliofilm" (rubber hydrochloride)	10	14	10
Polyvinyl chloride	10	19	70
Polyvinylidene chloride	14	20	20
Polyester	1	4	8
Cellulose acetate	5	5	5
Miscellaneous	1	3	5
Total	640	877	1,340

* Less than 3 mils thickness.
** Estimates from Modern Packaging Encyclopedia, 1960–1967.

Plastic Films.   The term "plastic films" encompasses an ever-increasing number of self-supporting, transparent films, each tailored to specific marketing requirements. Over 1.3 billion pounds of transparent films were produced in 1967 for consumption by the packaging industry. This total includes 385 million pounds of cellophane. Cellophane dominated the transparent film market prior to 1958, when the total packaging market was just over 600 million pounds. The consumption of cellophane has decreased slowly since 1960, when sales peaked at 440 million pounds. The growth of plastic film markets since 1958 has been largely that of polyethylene film. Its consumption has increased from 180 million pounds in 1958 to over 750 million pounds in 1967. Rapid growth rates were enjoyed by other thermoplastic films, but none have so far achieved the volume of cellophane or polyethylene. The remainder of the market is divided among other thermoplastics as listed in Table 1.1. Polyvinylchloride and polypropylene are expected to be the next large volume films.

The sophistication of packaging, development of new and improved packaging machinery, availability of new polymers for film and film coating uses, and competitive pressure for existing packaging film markets are factors which have combined to make possible a wide variety of films. Films holding significant portions of the market are discussed below, roughly in historical order. The discussion of plastic films must, of course, start with cellophane.

Cellophane. In 1892 Cross, Bevan, and Beadle discovered that a soluble cellulose could be prepared by digestion in sodium hydroxide followed by treatment with carbon disulfide. This reaction is essentially identical to the process used today. Purified wood pulp is digested in sodium hydroxide, then treated with carbon disulfide to produce cellulose xanthate. This "viscose" is extruded, then passed through a coagulation bath where the regeneration of cellulose occurs. After regeneration the film is submitted to various treatments to neutralize, bleach, wash, and plasticize it. It is then dried to a predetermined moisture content to maintain strength and flexibility. Coatings to impart moistureproofness, heat sealability, slip, and block resistance can then be applied.

Jacques Brandenberger, a Swiss chemist working with a French textile firm, is the Prince of Serendip of the film industry. He tried to invent an easily cleanable table cloth coating, by applying a thin sheet of viscose film to the cloth. Whatever the merits of the table cloth coating, which failed, the viscose film looked interesting to Brandenberger. He worked on to perfect thin gauges, designed a machine in 1911 to produce continuous lengths, and named his invention cellophane (*CELLU*LOSE plus the French word, DIA*PHANE*, meaning transparent).

Shortly before World War I the first cellophane plant was built in France. In 1923 E. I. duPont de Nemours & Company obtained the American rights, and in 1924 was selling cellophane for $2.65 a pound.

It was first used to wrap luxury items such as perfume. In 1927 duPont chemists W. H. Charch and K. E. Prindle developed a moistureproof coating. The coating comprised a nitrocellulose lacquer containing a small quantity of wax which was incompatible with the nitrocellulose. When the coating was dried, the wax migrated to the surface to form a thin layer of wax which reduced the permeability to water vapor. The nitrocellulose part of the coating provided heat sealability. After moistureproof, heat sealable, cellophanes were developed, packaging machines were designed to handle them automatically. Today, more than one hundred and twenty grades of cellophane are produced, including three levels of nitrocellulose-coated moistureproof film, for controlled moisture vapor transmission; and premium grades are coated with polyvinylidene chloride resin for maximum impermeability to moisture or gas.

Cellulose Acetate. Cellulose acetate film, today one of the premium packaging films, was first introduced in 1930. It is now used for window boxes, protective covers for books, displays and the like, where maximum brilliance, transparency and abrasion resistance are required. Cellulose acetate is prepared by dissolving cotton linters or purified wood pulp in acetic acid, acetic anhydride, and sulfuric acid. After the syrup has ripened or hydrolyzed, it is diluted with aqueous acetic acid solution to precipitate cellulose acetate flakes. The flakes are washed, dried, and plasticized to make them thermoplastic at a workable temperature. Films can be produced by casting or extrusion of these resins.

Cellulose Ethers. Several investigators studied cellulose ethers simultaneously in the period 1900–1920. Ethyl cellulose was prepared in 1916, but not until about 1930 did films become available. It is soluble in almost every type of organic solvent but insoluble in water. Films and sheets are manufactured by extruding a viscous solution of a high molecular weight ethyl cellulose onto a moving endless belt, which is passed through ovens to evaporate the solvent; the film or sheet can then be stripped from the belt. High cost has prevented expansion of ethyl cellulose into large markets.

Rubber Hydrochloride. Known commercially as "Pliofilm,"* rubber hydrochloride film was introduced by Goodyear in 1934. It was

* Registered trade name.

the first noncellulosic, thermoplastic, transparent film. Its thermoplasticity allowed it to be heat sealable to a welded bond. "Pliofilm" is produced by adding hydrogen chloride gas to a special grade of natural crude rubber in benzene solution. The solution is cast onto a continuous belt and passed through ovens to remove the solvent. Inclusion of waxes, plasticizers, or resins in the casting solution gives the finished film desired surface and bulk properties. "Pliofilm's " chief uses are in the packaging of cheese, fresh and prepared meat, and in laminations to upgrade foil, cellophane and paper.

Vinyl Film. Vinyls, which first appeared before World War II, include cast, calendered, and extruded films, that may be variously copolymers of vinyl chloride and vinyl acetate, or plasticized polyvinyl chloride and copolymers. These films appeared at a difficult time. Introduced in Europe, they first appeared in the United States just in time to have commercial development curtailed by the war effort.

Not until the early fifties did broadened activity again arise, when Union Carbide introduced vinyl cast film and Goodyear introduced "Vitafilm"* extruded polyvinyl chloride. Development of shrink wrapping techniques and oriented shrinkable vinyl films has brightened the future for vinyls.

Polyvinylidene Chloride. "Saran"* polyvinylidene chloride co-polymer film was hustled out of the test tube into limited production by the Dow Chemical Company during World War II to meet military requirements for a film having exceptionally good gas and water vapor barrier properties. It was used to package precision parts such as optical equipment, aircraft engines, guns, bombsights and computers.

Polyvinylidene chloride copolymer film is used for wrapping food-stuffs which are particularly sensitive to moisture loss, or to oxygen. Because of its high density and highly developed crystalline structure, even thin gauges of this material have high impermeability to gas and water vapor.

Polyethylene. Polyethylene is produced by the catalytic polymerization of ethylene under high pressure and temperature. These thermoplastic resins can be made in a range of densities, melting points, and linearity with varying strength, flexibility, and melting temperatures.

* Registered trade name.

To date, the most useful films are made from low and medium density resins.

Polyethylene was introduced in 1939 by Imperial Chemical Industries in England. Film was first produced in 1945 by the Visking Corporation by using a blown extruded tube. Large quantities of resin were available because of the existence of wartime production facilities for the manufacture of polyethylene electrical insulation. As late as 1949, however, some polyethylene film was still being produced by solvent casting and calendering. By 1951, hot extrusion processes utilizing both straight and circular dies had won out, and polyethylene was becoming one of the most economical packaging films. Polyethylene film markets and uses grew phenomenally, and in 1963 surpassed cellophane in pound volume.

Polyester. In 1954 duPont began to produce "Mylar"* polyester film in quantity. It is the condensation product of ethylene glycol and terephthalic acid. Polyesters are a family of films characterized by exceptional strength over a wide temperature range, high dielectric constant, and good solvent resistance. In 1957 polyester cook-and-serve packages were introduced; the high heat resistance of the film allowed it to be immersed in boiling water. Introduction of heat sealable, coated polyesters in the sixties has enabled polyester films to serve in many new applications.

Polystyrene. Polystyrene is a thermoplastic which was first discovered in storax, a natural resin from trees. In 1911 use patents were taken out. Thin foils developed in Europe in the thirties were used for electric cable insulation. Introduced commercially in the United States by The Dow Chemical Company in the thirties, polystyrene had gained the volume of a commodity by the fifties. Oriented polystyrene film was introduced in 1948 and has since found utility in thin gauges as an overwrap, in window boxes, window envelopes, and cartons and in thicker gauges as a pressure or vacuum formable sheet.

Polypropylene. This plastic is produced from propylene in processes similar to those used for polyethylene. Polypropylene film was introduced in 1960. It is available in three basic forms:

(1) Unoriented, produced by chill roll casting.

(2) Non heat set, oriented film for shrink wrapping.

* Registered trade name.

(3) Oriented, heat set for maximum heat resistance. Functionality of this type of film has been increased by the addition of coatings which confer improved heat sealability and barrier properties.

New films are continually appearing on the scene. Recent newcomers include nylon, fluorohalocarbons, polycarbonate, irradiated polyethylène, polyvinyl fluoride, polyvinylidene fluoride, polymethyl methacrylate, polyoxymethylene, and polyurethane films. Polyvinyl alcohol, polyethylene oxide, and methyl cellulose films have been developed as water soluble films for unit packages of detergents and bleaches. Potential applications include unit packaging of water soluble or dispersible foods and drugs. Other new films are developed nearly as rapidly as new plastics become available.

It appears likely that the technology of plastic films will continue to expand at least as rapidly as plastics technology itself and that plastic films will play an ever increasing role in our industrial, scientific, and domestic economy.

TWO

methods of manufacture

W. R. R. PARK

Most plastics can be made into both oriented and unoriented films, and while some of the processes are similar in concept, they differ widely in detail. Also, oriented and unoriented films of the same material differ broadly in properties. For these reasons, this chapter is divided into two main sections which discuss fabrication methods for unoriented and for oriented films. In addition brief descriptions of papermaking and aluminum foil fabrication are included, since these two materials are so often used in combination with plastic films and plastic coatings.

Papermaking. Paper consists largely of pure cellulose fibers, which have been separated from the other components that constitute various types of wood. These individual and separate fibers are recombined to give paper of various qualities. The wide spectrum of paper properties which are available today results from the great variety of raw materials, additives, processing, coating, and finishing variables that can be used. Figure 2.1 illustrates a sequence of operations which is typical of conventional papermaking, and Figure 2.2 gives an indication of the complexity of the equipment required in a modern, continuous high-speed papermaking machine.

Aluminum Foil. Most metals can be made into thin foils by adaptation of steel rolling techniques. So far, only aluminum foil has

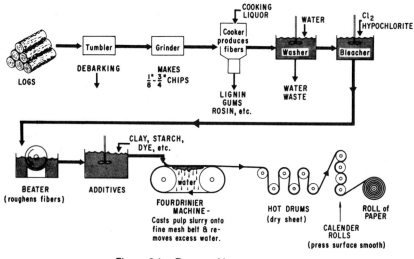

Figure 2.1.   Papermaking.

Figure 2.2.   "Wet end" of a papermaking machine. (*Courtesy of S. D. Warren Co.*)

found widespread utility. This material, in thicknesses down to .0002 inch, is widely used in packaging because, when properly handled, it is completely impermeable to water, gases, odors, and solvents. The thinner gauges, by themselves, are quite weak and easily ruptured, but when combined with plastic films such as polyvinylidene chloride or polyester, or when extrusion coated with polyolefins they become functional packaging materials that provide the best possible protective barrier/cost ratios. Aluminum foil is found in all packaging fabrications which require the best barrier properties attainable from flexible packaging materials.

Aluminum foil is made by passing hot sheet through a series of hot, highly polished, precision finished metal roll nips of ever decreasing nip openings until the desired final thickness of foil is obtained. Foil is generally made from nearly pure aluminum. Some grades will be alloyed with up to 1–1.5% manganese where higher strength is needed. Depending on the degree of tempering and chemical composition, foils are generally made within the following limits of physical properties:

Ultimate tensile, psi	10,000–30,000
Yield strength, psi	4,500–27,000
Elongation, %	37–4
Brinell hardness	20–55

Since, in laminations, extensibility is generally more important than tensile strength, the lower strength, higher elongation grades are preferred. In thicker gauges, when aluminum is used by itself, as in can manufacture, tensile strength may be the more important property. Figure 2.3 shows a typical aluminum foil rolling mill in operation.

UNORIENTED FILM AND SHEET

Flat Sheet Extrusion. Virtually any thermoplastic material can be fabricated into film or sheet form by melt extrusion through a slot die. A typical extrusion line for plastic sheet is shown in Figure 2.4. Such lines can be used to produce sheets up to six feet wide and ranging in thickness from less than .010 inch up to .250 inch.

When thinner sheets or films are desired, a modification of this line is employed, as illustrated in Figure 2.5. Here a single cooling roll suffices to chill the plastic, since heat transfer is very rapid through thin plastic films. An air knife exerts an hydraulic pressure on the molten web to assure intimate contact with the cooling drum. In sheet extrusion, both sides of the sheet contact cooling surfaces. Another significant difference in operation is that the extrudate is drastically thinned out between the die and the cooling drum in film extrusion. Typically, the die opening may be .020 inch while the finished film may be less than .001 inch thick. This setup, when running films of less than .001 inch thickness, may operate at speeds in excess of 500 fpm and, thus, needs a multiple shaft rewind station to ensure continuous operation. Films

Figure 2.3.   This 78 inch, 4-high foil rolling mill produces aluminum foil for Reynolds Wrap, foil packaging materials, and other products. (*Courtesy of Reynolds Metal Co.*)

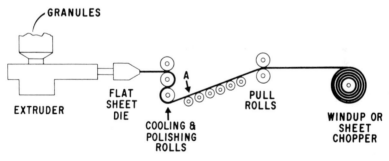

Figure 2.4.   Plastic sheet extrusion. Chill roll casting.

ranging in thickness from .00025 inch to .020 inch are conveniently manufactured on this type of equipment.

There is an overlap in the capabilities of these two extrusion lines as far as thickness of product is concerned. The question of definition of film and sheet thicknesses arises. No industry standard has so far been recognized. An arbitrary division line, which has been found convenient,

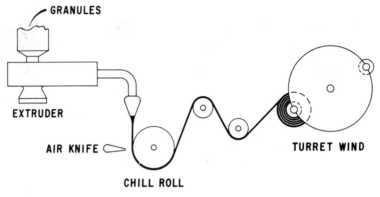

Figure 2.5.   Plastic film extrusion. Chill roll casting.

defines sheet as thicker than 3 mils and film as 3 mils and thinner. This definition will be used throughout this book.

Gauge Profile Control.   Both of these film and sheet extrusion lines have problems in maintaining uniform thickness profiles across the sheet. As a result, the dies are equipped with adjusting nuts across their width. Usually the die opening is adjusted while the unit is cold. When running, thermal stresses and small differences in flow rates in different parts of the die usually require that further die opening adjustments be made. Until recently, these adjustments were generally made by hand after manually checking the gauge profile with a micrometer. As a result, considerable running time was needed to obtain sheet having a satisfactory gauge profile. This time was shortened through the use of a β ray thickness scanner, typically installed at point "A" in Figure 2.4. This accessory gives continuous and accurate gauge profile readings, which allows more rapid manual adjustment of the die to satisfactory thickness tolerances. This type of instrumentation can be completely automated. Industrial Nucleonics Corporation has developed a system using a gauge profile sensing head, which feeds signals back to a specially designed jig, that automatically changes the die openings to compensate for gauge variations. It is expected that this type of equipment, when perfected, will provide improved gauge, higher yields, less scrap, faster start up, and safer working conditions. It has the additional advantage of continuous compensation, which is needed in even the finest equipment, because gauge does vary with time due to a number of factors. In thin films it is projected that a $\pm$ 2% gauge variation can automatically be obtained with this equipment. Continuous manual adjustment of die openings seldom produces film with better than $\pm$ 5% gauge variation and $\pm$ 10% is not uncommon.

Gauge control becomes critical when film or thin sheeting, which will remain flat, is required. Obviously, any film extruded from a slot die is initially flat regardless of its gauge profile. However, when wound on a roll under sufficient tension to prevent telescoping, any thick sections which are allowed to remain in the material will pile up on themselves, so that the roll is very hard at these points and soft at all others. This creates high stress at the hard spots and at some stress level which varies for each material, the elastic limit of the film will be exceeded and the film on the roll will undergo permanent deformation at the high spots. When unrolled, this initially flat film will exhibit "bag" properties, since it is longer in some fibers than in others, and it can no longer be made to lay flat.

One obvious means of overcoming this tendency is to extrude film which has no sections thick enough to cause development of "bag" when wound up. Industrial Nucleonics Corporation is attempting to do this by preventing the occurrence of gauge bands through gauge profile control. Obviously, the plus and minus gauge tolerance which will prevent "bag" development will be different for each material and will also depend on the winding tensions which are used.

Where it is not found possible to control gauge tolerance sufficiently closely to prevent "bag" development, other systems must be used. These are gauge randomization systems. The least effective and probably the least expensive technique involves slowly oscillating the whole rewind stand a few inches perpendicular to the direction of film travel. Gauge bands are spread over a wider area, and their "bag" producing effect may be eliminated in some cases and alleviated in almost all instances. This technique has the disadvantage of requiring a wider edge trim and, thus, generates a greater percentage of scrap or recycle material than the use of a stationary windup with conventional edge trim.

Another more complex method for achieving gauge randomization consists of using a die wider than needed. The desired film width is obtained by blocking off each end of the slot with fixed deckle rods. The die is slowly oscillated back and forth on these stationary deckle rods, and the thick film sections, thus, become smeared over a greater lateral area. This randomization technique is somewhat cumbersome since the extruder also has to be oscillated. Figure 2.6 illustrates this principle.

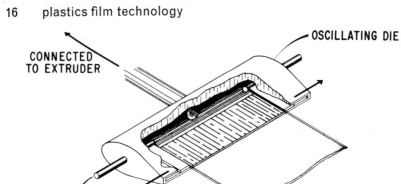

CONNECTED
TO EXTRUDER

OSCILLATING DIE

STATIONARY
DECKLE ROD

Figure 2.6.   Die oscillator.

A randomizing technique which appears well suited to sheet extrusion is illustrated in Figure 2.7. Here, the die remains stationary, but the choke bar oscillates back and forth, causing the lateral smearing of gauge bands through its shearing effect on the hot melt. Other variations are possible.

Generally, unless it proves possible to adjust the die to extrude uniform thickness of either film or sheet, some type of randomization technique can be used to advantage wherever flatness is critical.

Die Design.   Die geometry can be critical to a successful film or sheet extrusion operation. Any heat sensitive polymer, such as polyvinyl chloride (PVC), cannot be practically extruded through the relatively simple dies used on polystyrene type materials. Unless the die is highly streamlined, PVC tends to degrade and discolor at any point where its flow rate is slow or where stagnant pockets of hot polymer can form. The two extreme types of die design in current usage, shown in Figure 2.8 are the T-die and coat hanger die. The former is much less expensive to fabricate and has proven adequate for materials

HOT
POLYMER

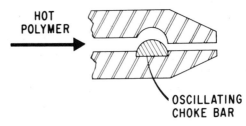

OSCILLATING
CHOKE BAR

Figure 2.7.   Choke bar oscillator.

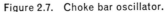

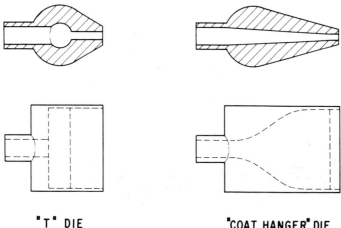

"T" DIE   "COAT HANGER" DIE

Figure 2.8.   Die types.

which are relatively insensitive to heat. The latter is used with heat sensitive material, since there are no areas wherein the polymer can hang up and degrade.

MATERIALS FABRICATED BY SLOT EXTRUSION

Cellophane. All cellophanes are made by a slot extrusion process which differs from thermoplastic film extrusion in that a viscose solution (dissolved cellulose) is extruded into an acid bath, which insolubilizes and regenerates the dissolved cellulose. A typical sequence of operations is sketched in Figure 2.9 and illustrated in 2.10 and 2.11. This plain cellophane is ready for coating, which is discussed in detail in Chapter 3.

Polyethylene and Polypropylene. Polyolefin films that are made by the chill roll method (Figure 2.5), are seldom thicker than .005 inch or thinner than .00035 inch. Since a die opening of .020 inch is common, it is obvious that a high degree of machine direction stretching must occur between the die and the chill roll. This can lead to problems if the extrusion temperature is too low, since the film will be oriented in the machine direction (MD). This makes it stronger in this direction, but leads also to a tendency to split in the machine direction. Thus, it is necessary to extrude at a sufficiently high temperature, so that the hot stretch orientation largely relaxes out before the web is chilled. Extrusion temperatures of 525–600°F give a minimum of difficulty in this regard. This effect, however, can still be detected in any

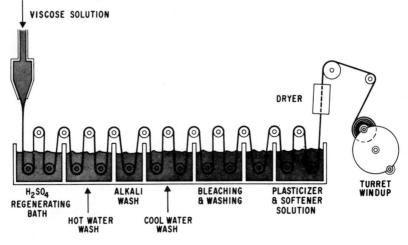

Figure 2.9.   Cellophane extrusion.

Figure 2.10.   Cellophane production line. Cellophane enters one end of this 200 ft long casting machine at the duPont Company's Richmond, Va., plant as a liquid and is wound up at the other end as a dry shiny film. On its way through the machine, a series of baths purify, wash, and soften the film, after which it is dried. A casting machine represents an investment of $500,000. For efficient, economical production, a cellophane plant must include 8 similar units, together with an array of other specially designed equipment for other vital process steps. Altogether, resources of at least $20,000,000 and a host of trained specialists are needed to design, build, and operate such a plant. (*Courtesy of E. I. duPont de Nemours & Co.*)

Figure 2.11.   Windup end of cellophane production unit. A mill roll of cellophane is being taken away from a casting machine at the duPont Company's Tecumseh, Kansas, cellophane plant. A single mill roll may contain as much as 8 miles of cellophane. The Tecumseh plant, which made its first commercial shipments in December, 1958, is able to produce 50,000,000 lb of cellophane a year, a quantity equivalent to a strip of cellophane 5 ft wide that would encircle the earth 10 times at the equator. (*Courtesy of E. I. duPont de Nemours & Co.*)

films made in this manner by comparing the machine and transverse direction (MD and TD) physical properties. Table 2.1 shows that chill roll cast films have higher MD tensile strength and lower MD tear strength. These properties are typical of film having some MD and no TD orientation.

TABLE 2.1.   Unbalanced MD–TD Properties of Chill Roll Cast Films

	Tensile Strength (psi)		Elmendorf Tear (gm)	
	MD*	TD**	MD	TD
1 Mil polyethylene	2,800	2,200	60	150
1 Mil polypropylene	5,700	3,200	50	550

* Machine direction.
** Transverse direction.

Cellulose Esters and Ethers.   Cellulose acetate, propionate, acetate-butyrate, and butyrate, as well as ethyl cellulose, may be made into film and sheet by flat die extrusion techniques. Relatively high plasticizer contents are required in these resins to obtain satisfactory melt flow properties for extrusion. Lower plasticizer contents can generally be used in resins that are solution cast and cast films have, as a result, somewhat better physical properties. Also, solution cast cellulosic films tend to have smoother, more flawless surfaces than melt extruded materials where die lines can never be completely eliminated. A typical solution casting line is shown in Figure 2.12.

Other Extrudable Plastics. In addition to cellophane, polyolefins, and cellulosic derivatives, many other plastics can be and have been successfully extruded to give film and sheet. Extrusion conditions, die designs, takeaway equipment, materials of construction, types of extruders, etc., generally have to be selected to meet the requirements of the particular material or even the particular grade of a single material which is to be extruded.

The following materials have been made into film and/or sheet by flat extrusion techniques:

Rigid PVC (zero or low plasticizer content—may be copolymer)
Flexible PVC (plasticized)
Polycarbonates
Nylon
Polyvinylidene fluoride
Polyester (nonoriented type)
Phenoxy-8 (a bisphenol type polymer)
Polyvinyl acetals
Chlorinated polyethylene
Methyl cellulose
Polyethylene oxide

Polyvinylbutyral
Polymonochlorotrifluoroethylene
FEP resins (fluorinated ethylene-propylene)
H film (high temperature resistant polyimide)
Teflon (polytetrafluoroethylene)
Chlorinated polyether
Acrylics
Rubber modified polystyrenes (high impact for forming)
ABS (acrylonitrile, butadiene and styrene copolymers)

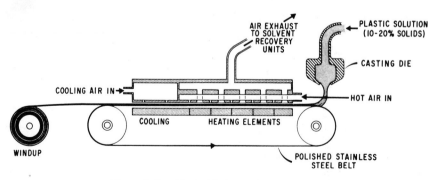

Figure 2.12. Typical belt casting operation.

Shaped Extrusion. For some packaging applications, sheet can be extruded in a finished shape instead of as flat stock. Generally these shaped extrusions use 10–20 mil material, which is extruded in the form of cylinders, half rounds, squares, rectangles, trapezoids, ovals, hexagons, etc. Most shapes are from two to eight inches in length and from less than one half to about ten inches in circumference. The most commonly used materials are cellulose acetate, butrate and propionate, which give clarity, toughness and rigidity. Other materials, such as polyethylene, polypropylene, vinyl, and nylon can also be shaped by extrusion, particularly where squeeze tubes with specific flex and chemical resistance properties are the desired end products. The open ends of these extruded shapes may be treated in a number of ways: rolled in or out for snap closures, provided with a straight edge for plug closures, or swedged for formed closures. This shaped extrusion technique is the least expensive way to arrive at a number of different container configurations and will probably find increasing use in the future. Typical available cross sections are shown in Figure 2.13.

Bubble Process. A number of film and thin plastic sheet materials (seldom over 10 mils thickness) are made by the so-called bubble process. In this process a relatively thick walled tube is extruded (up, down, or sideways), then expanded in the transverse direction while being accelerated in the machine or extrusion direction. This is accomplished by trapping a bubble of air inside the expanded tube. The polyethylene bubble process is illustrated in Figure 2.14, and a typical equipment line is shown in Figure 2.15.

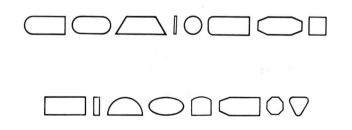

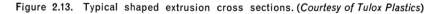

Figure 2.13. Typical shaped extrusion cross sections. (*Courtesy of Tulox Plastics*)

Where needed, gauge randomization is achieved by one or a combination of the following techniques:

(1) Rotate or oscillate the entire collapsing and windup assembly.
(2) Rotate die mandrel.
(3) Rotate or oscillate extruder and die assembly.
(4) Rotate air cooling ring.

Extrusion temperatures are generally kept as low as practical, so that, with the aid of the air ring, the temperature of the blown film will fall rapidly. Thus, the extrudate quickly develops sufficient tensile strength so that the bubble can be stabilized. High extrusion temperatures cause the bubble to weave from side to side or may even cause it to blow out near the die where the polymer viscosity is still very low.

Low density polyethylene (.5–10 mils), polyvinylchloride, polyamides (nylon type), polystyrene foam film and sheet, and methyl cellulose can be made by modifications of this basic process.

Solution Casting.   Where the best surface properties are desired in plastic film and sheet, it can be made by solvent casting. In this process plastic granules or powder, plus any desired formulant such as

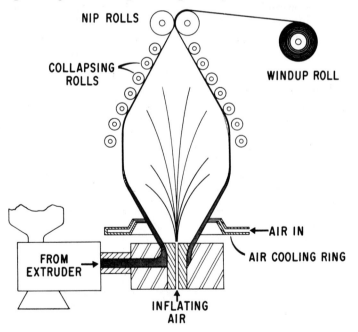

Figure 2.14.   Bubble process for polyethylene film.

Figure 2.15.   A typical polyethylene bubble unit. Sterling extruder
and blown film tower. Included are an extruder, a die, an air ring,
converging roll section and a windup station. (Equipment made
by Sterling Extruder Corp.)

plasticizer or colorant, are dissolved in a suitable solvent. The solution
is carefully filtered to remove any dirt or gel particles, then cast, from
a slot die, onto a moving, endless, highly polished stainless steel belt.
The solvent is removed by controlled heating and solvent free, sparkling
clear, flat film is stripped from the takeoff section of the casting belt, as
shown in Figure 2.12.

Gauge control is achieved by adjusting the die opening across its
width. The extrudate thickness is five to ten times that of the finished
film, and the die can be adjusted to $\pm$ 1–2% gauge variation on such
thicknesses. Thus, the dried film thickness variation is also $\pm$ 1–2%.
Gauge control that can be achieved on melt extrusion of the same final
film thickness is seldom better than $\pm$ 5–10%. In addition, then, to
giving the best optical grades of film and sheet, solution casting can

consistently produce more uniform gauge film than can be made by melt extrusion with current technology.

Most commonly, cellulose acetate, butyrate, and propionate, as well as ethyl cellulose films are made by solution casting. Other materials which can be or have been made into film and sheet by this technique are polyvinyl chloride, and vinyl chloride-vinyl acetate copolymers, polymethyl methacrylate, polycarbonate, and polyvinyl alcohol.

Two other types of films that can be made by belt casting techniques are polytetrafluoroethylene ("Teflon"*) and polyvinyl fluoride ("Tedlar"*). These polymers, which are virtually insoluble in any solvents, can be prepared in aqueous dispersions, then cast on a belt and fused to continuous pinhole free films at temperatures well below their melting points. Since these materials are very difficult or impossible to extrude conventionally, belt casting provides a convenient means for their fabrication into film and sheet.

The Calendering Process. In this process continuous sheets of controlled thickness are formed by squeezing a heated plastic material between two or more horizontal rollers. Polyvinyl chloride accounts for most of the flexible film and sheet which is made by this process. Machinery has been developed to make film less than 2 mils thick, up to 10 feet wide, at speeds in excess of 300 fpm, having tolerances of 1/10 mil.

In a typical processing sequence, polyvinyl chloride resin is formulated with plasticizer, colorants, heat stabilizers, etc., and the formulation is thoroughly mixed in a Banbury mixer. When homogeneous, this mix is fed through a two roll mill to give heavy sheet stock, which in turn is fed to the calender, where it is reduced to the desired width, thickness, and surface finish (see Figure 2.16). Since the calender rolls are precision finished and operate at high nip pressure and narrow gap settings, it is important that no metallic contaminants be introduced. Thus, metal detectors are almost always included in the line to prevent roll damage.

In addition to the wide variety of polyvinyl chloride films and sheets which are processed by calendering, such materials as polyurethane rubber, ethylene-propylene copolymers, ethylene-vinyl acetate copolymers, ethylene-ethyl acrylate copolymers, and rubber modified polystyrene have been fabricated into sheet stock on units similar to that shown in Figure 2.17.

* Registered trade name.

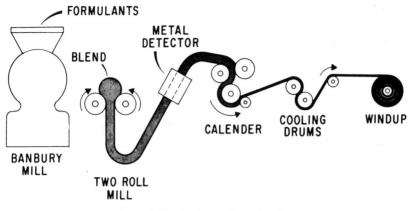

Figure 2.16.   Typical calendering line.

Skiving. This method, which consists of cutting thin sheets continuously from cylindrical billets to convert them into lengths of film or sheet, has been used to prepare polytetrafluoroethylene ("Teflon") film. Some types of foamed polystyrene sheet have also been prepared by this method, which is illustrated in Figure 2.18. This method finds utility only when no other fabrication techniques can be made to work or else are excessively expensive.

Figure 2.17.   A production calender for plastic sheet. 28 in. × 84 in. four roll inverted Ell calender with roll bending equipment and pinion stand drive. (*Courtesy of Adamson United*).

BIAXIALLY ORIENTED FILM AND SHEET

Biaxial orientation is a process whereby a plastic film or sheet is stretched in such a way as to orient the polymeric chains of the plastic parallel to the plane of the film, but more or less randomly within this plane. Biaxially oriented films possess superior tensile, flexibility, toughness, and shrinkability properties in comparison with their nonoriented counterparts.

Virtually any thermoplastic material can be oriented. The types which already have proven commercial utility are the following:

polyvinylidene chloride*   polypropylene
polystyrene*   irradiated polyethylene
polyesters   rubber hydrochloride
polyvinyl chloride*   polymethyl methacrylate
polyvinyl fluoride

These are available in thicknesses ranging from .00015 inch up to about .060 inch with varying levels of orientation.

The first biaxial orientation process was developed in Germany about 1935 and was used during World War II to manufacture oriented polystyrene film for capacitors and coaxial cable insulation. In the late 1940's Dow Chemical introduced oriented "Saran" polyvinylidene chloride film, and in 1954 duPont started to sell oriented "Mylar" polyester film. These latter two materials are typical of materials that can be made by the two major orientation processes in use today—namely the tubular or bubble process and the flat sheet or tentering technique.

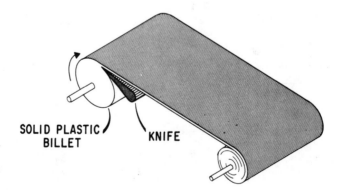

SOLID PLASTIC BILLET   KNIFE

Figure 2.18. Skiving.

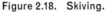

* May be modified by copolymerization with up to 40 % of one or more other monomers.

Theory of Stress-Induced Orientation.   In stress-induced orientation, polymer chains are displaced, by hot stretching or drawing the bulk material, from a completely random entanglement into a more orderly arrangement parallel to the direction of stress. When chain straightening has occurred, and with the closer packing that accompanies molecular alignment, mutual attraction between the chains is increased, since they are now in a position to exert the greatest possible secondary valence forces on each other. These are particularly large if the chains are symmetrical and/or strongly polar. This, and the unfolding of the polymer chains, result in increased tensile strength and elastic modulus, and, with the anisotropic nature of the state, account for the distinctive characteristics of an oriented polymer.

Molecular orientation during stretching takes place in the following manner. Below their glass transition temperatures (Tg), polymer chains are rigid. However, at the glass transition temperature they gain a degree of freedom and become able to unfold as stress is applied. If a mass of randomly coiled and entangled chains is at a temperature (above Tg) where it may be drawn out, then, when stress is applied, as in biaxial stretching, the polymer chains disentangle and straighten and also slip past one another.

There are three components to this process: E_1, the instantaneous elastic deformation caused by valence angle deformation or bond stretching, and which is completely recoverable when the stress is removed; E_2, the molecular alignment deformation caused by uncoiling, which results in a more linear molecular arrangement parallel to the surface, and which is frozen into the structure when the material is cooled; E_3, the nonrecoverable viscous flow caused by molecules sliding past one another.

E_2 is the orienting component, the one desired to be the major component of the stretching process.

On the basis of the above theory, some general rules for orienting polymers by stretching can be set forth:

(1) The lowest stretching temperature above Tg will give the greatest orientation (and greatest tensile strength, etc.) at a given percent and rate of stretch. E_3, flow, is held to a minimum by keeping the temperature as low as possible (see Figure 2.19).

(2) The highest stretch rate will give the greatest orientation at a given temperature and percent stretch. Since E_3 is slower than E_2, E_2 will predominate during rapid stretching.

(3) The highest percent stretch will give the greatest orientation at a given temperature and rate of stretch (see Figure 2.19).

(4) The greatest quench rate will preserve the most orientation under any stretching condition.

Types of Orientation.   *Uniaxial* orientation takes place during the drawing of a filament. Here the polymer chains are aligned in one dimension, as in a sheaf. This produces maximum strength in one direction, that of orientation. The tensile strength of nylon, for example, can be increased from 10,000 psi to over 80,000 psi by drawing. Although desirable in a fiber, a uniaxially oriented film tends to crack and split along lines parallel to the direction of stretching.

Biaxial or planar orientation occurs when a film or sheet is drawn in more than one direction, commonly along two axes at right angles to one another. The tensile strength and elastic modulus are increased in the directions of pull and decreased in the direction perpendicular to the plane of the film. Since the polymer chains are here oriented in a web parallel to the surface rather than to one another as in the uniaxially oriented fiber, the level of tensile properties attainable, although significantly above that for unoriented film, is not as great as for that of fibers (Table 2.2).

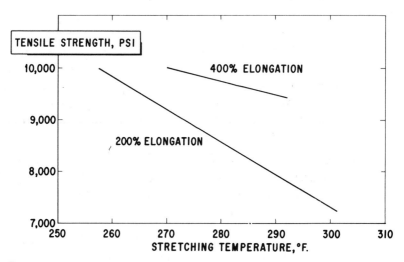

Figure 2.19.   Enhancement of room temperature strength through orientation is a function of both temperature and % elongation for polystyrene.

TABLE 2.2.   Effect of Orientation on Physical Properties of Polyethylene Terephthalate*

	Tensile Strength (psi)	Elongation at break (%)	Yield Stress (psi)
Unstretched	6,000	500	6,000
Biaxially stretched	25,000	130	10,000
Uniaxially stretched	>75,000	7	>75,000

* Mylar.

Balance in biaxial orientation is the result of the relative degree of stretching in the different directions during the orientation process. Uniform planar orientation or balanced biaxial orientation is actually only one special case in a continuous spectrum of degrees of orientation and is less frequently encountered than are slightly or grossly unbalanced orientations. For most oriented film applications it is desirable to have a film as nearly balanced as practicable, since these films will behave in the same manner, or nearly so, from any direction. As the percent stretch becomes greater in one direction than in another, values of properties in the one direction increase at the expense of those in the other direction.

Although a film of balanced orientation is desirable for most purposes, there are some applications, such as those involving shrinkage or a greater tensile strength in one direction, in which a film of unbalanced orientation is preferred.

Uses.   An example which can utilize an unbalanced orientation is nylon strapping material, which is being introduced to replace steel strapping. Here, strength is needed in the lengthwise direction only, and this type of orientation provides a strap which will shrink to some extent in this direction if the package decreases in dimension, but will not shrink in the cross direction. Also, a higher tensile strength can be obtained by uniaxial than by biaxial stretching. Pressure sensitive tape backings and recording tapes are also more highly oriented in the lengthwise direction, but generally require some orientation in the cross direction to overcome the fibrillation tendencies of uniaxially oriented film.

Shrinkage Behavior of Oriented Amorphous Plastics.   Oriented polystyrene film typifies the behavior of biaxially oriented noncrystallizable polymers. This material, on gradual unrestrained heating, shows only a thermal expansion until the region of the second order transition or glass temperature, Tg, is reached. At temperatures above Tg, the material will shrink. The rate of shrink increases with increasing temperature.

When a sample of biaxially oriented polystyrene film is heated and restrained from shrinking, it loses orientation but not as rapidly as if free to shrink (see Figure 2.20). Also, a restrained sample shows an orientation release stress when heated. That is, the material exerts a positive pull on the restraining clamps in its attempt to shrink. The magnitude of this release stress is related to the original film stretching conditions and gives another measure of orientation level, although this does not always correlate with the amount of shrink in any given sample.

Finally, there is no known way to stabilize an oriented film of an amorphous plastic against shrinkage above its glass transition temperature.

Shrinkage Behavior of Oriented Crystallizable Plastics.   The main difference between crystallizable and noncrystallizable polymers in oriented form is that the crystallizable type can be stabilized against gross shrinkage above their glass transition temperatures. Thus, it is possible to make two film samples of the same material having the same degree of orientation and greatly different shrinkage behavior at a given temperature.

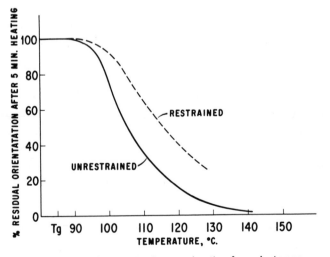

Figure 2.20. Orientation loss on heating for polystyrene.

For example, if polyethylene terephthalate is melted at 290°C, then rapidly quenched to below its Tg, 69°C, an essentially amorphous material is obtained. When rapidly stretched at 90°C, then quenched, this material shows essentially the same behavior on reheating as oriented polystyrene. That is, when heated unrestrained above Tg, it starts to shrink, and its shrink rate increases to a maximum as the original stretch temperature is approached or exceeded. Essentially, then, under these conditions, polyethylene terephthalate behaves exactly like any amorphous polymeric material.

When an extra processing step is introduced into the foregoing melt, quench, heat, stretch, and quench sequence, a film can be obtained which has nearly identical room temperature physical properties (tensile, elongation, etc.), but which has negligible shrinkage at 100°C. This extra step involves restraining the film at its stretched dimension and heating briefly (a few seconds) to 150–225°C, then quenching as before. This additional heat treatment has the effect of heat stabilizing the oriented film. It can still be forced to shrink, but before it will do so to any appreciable extent, it must be reheated to the heat stabilization temperature or above.

Thus, it is possible, with crystallizable polymers, to stabilize the oriented film against gross shrinkage above Tg. This is indeed fortunate since the majority of commercially valuable crystalline polymers have glass transition temperatures below 25°C (see Table 2.3).

A second factor which plays an important role in the ability of crystallizable polymers to be first oriented and then heat stabilized is the relative ease or difficulty of amorphizing the material prior to stretching, or at least stabilizing the material at a low level of crystallinity. This step is necessary since it is not feasible to introduce a high level of biaxial orientation into a polymer film which has even a moderate crystalline content. Thus, for each crystalline material to be oriented, it is necessary to have a knowledge of its rate of crystallization over the temperature range from its glass transition temperature to its melting point (see "Saranpac"* in Chapter 4).

Heat Stabilization Mechanism of Oriented Crystalline Film. The shrink behavior of oriented amorphous polymers is a relatively simple phenomenon. When heated above their glass transition temperatures, the frozen–in orientation starts to relax out. A very simple experiment clearly demonstrates this behavior. A stretched rubber band immersed

* Registered trade name.

TABLE 2.3.   Glass Transition Temperatures of Common Plastics

Polymer	Tg (°C)	Crystalline Melting Point or Softening Point (°C)
Polyethylene—high density	− 120	135
Polyethylene—low density	− 25	98
Polyoxymethylene	− 50	185
Polyvinylfluoride ("Tedlar")	− 20	195
Polypropylene	0 to − 20	175
Polyvinylidene chloride ("Saran")	− 17	195
Polyvinyl acetate	29	up to 175
Polyhexamethylene adipamide (Nylon)	50	250
Polyethylene terephthalate ("Mylar")	69	255
Polystyrene	80–100(85)	105–110
Polyvinyl chloride		
No plasticizer	105	up to 212
15% plasticizer	60	
Cellulose acetate	70–120	up to 300
Polymethyl methacrylate	105	160
Polytetrafluoroethylene ("Teflon")	126	327
Polycarbonate	150	230

in a dry ice-alcohol mixture will retain its stretched dimension when the stress is removed. When taken out of the cold bath, the rubber band spontaneously reverts to its original dimension on warming up to room temperature.

Crystallizable polymers will also behave in this manner if they are kept in an amorphous condition. However, if a crystallizable polymer is oriented then heat treated under restraint at a higher temperature, crystallization can occur. When crystallization occurs from a random melt, it occurs in a random three dimensional manner. When crystallization occurs from an oriented planar melt (stretched amorphous condition), it is believed that the crystallites and spherulites also become two dimensionally oriented during their formation. As these crystallites and spherulites grow, they encompass and lock in place many molecular chains which are already aligned. Thus, these chains are not free to retract even though they are above the Tg for the bulk material. While crystallization does not completely immobilize oriented chains above their glass transition temperature, the mechanism works sufficiently well so that essentially stable films are obtained at room temperature.

Physical Properties of Oriented Films.   As pointed out in Table 2.2, biaxial orientation of plastics invariably increases tensile strength and decreases elongation. The magnitude of the effect of orientation varies with each polymeric material. The only other property which is significantly different from those found in the same unoriented plastics is dimensional stability. All oriented films will shrink to some degree at a temperature between their Tg's and their melting point. The amount and temperature of shrinkage initiation depends on the previous stretch and annealing history of the film. In the case of polypropylene, an extra benefit is obtained through orientation. Unoriented film is very brittle at below zero temperatures and has a tendency to shatter on impact when used as an overwrap for frozen goods. Biaxially oriented film remains flexible, when cold, to much lower temperatures.

Gas transmission rates and moisture vapor transmission rates for amorphous polymers, both oriented and non-oriented, appear to be nearly identical. Crystallizable polymers show minor differences, if any, in their permeability properties in stretched and unstretched conditions. In these types gas transmission rates are largely dependent on crystallite size and content, and these factors swamp out any effect introduced by orientation.

Shrink properties of crystalline polymers can be varied quite widely by processing conditions. Table 2.4 shows what can be done with saran films. Table 2.5 shows a variety of shrinkage behaviors which can be

TABLE 2.4.*   Shrink Properties of Saran Films

| | Shrinkage** | | Thickness–Mils | |
	MD	TD	Before Shrink	After Shrink
Unstabilized "Saran"	30%	40%	5	12
"Saran" stabilized under restraint at 120°C for 6 seconds	3%	3%	5	5

* Dow Chemical Company data.
** 5 minutes in boiling water.

TABLE 2.5.*   Shrink Properties of Polyester Films

| | % Shrink** 100°C | | % Shrink** 150°C | |
	MD	TD	MD	TD
Stabilized polyester	< 1	< 1	2	2
Shrinkable polyester A	46	18		
Shrinkable polyester B	30	35		
Shrinkable polyester B at 80°C	21	22		
Shrinkable polyester B at 70°C	2.5	2		

* Dow Chemical Company data.
** 15 minutes.

obtained with polyester films. These are all clear films and of the same chemical composition. The differing properties reflect differences in heat stabilization processing (crystalline content) and in the amount of stretch in the two directions.

In general, crystallizable films oriented by the bubble process will have more closely matched properties in MD and TD than is the case with tentered films. This is illustrated in Table 2.6 where properties of representative polypropylene films, oriented by these two methods, are compared. Theoretically, it is possible to achieve MD–TD balance by tentering, but, practically, it appears more difficult to do this with crystalline polymers than with amorphous types.

TABLE 2.6.†   Properties of Oriented Polypropylene***

	Film A*	Film B**
Thickness, mils	.60	.75
Tensile strength, psi ⎱ MD	26,300	17,500
ASTM–D 882–56T ⎰ TD	26,000	42,000
% Elongation ⎱ MD	45	120
ASTM–D 882–56T ⎰ TD	40	20
% shrink ⎱ MD	8	3.5
60 min at 124°C ⎰ TD	15	3.5

* Bubble process.
** Tenter process.
*** These properties were obtained on specific commercial samples and are not necessarily representative of the values attainable by either process.
† Dow Chemical Company data.

The effect of irradiation on polymeric materials has been widely investigated. One of the most successful applications has been the use of radiation to cross-link polyethylene film. In table 2.7 the properties of regular bubble-made polyethylene film are compared to those of irradiated film also made by a bubble-process. Cross-linking increases tensile strength, orientation release stress, and heat sealing range to make a practical shrink film from polyethylene. It has toughness properties similar to polyvinylidene chloride films and has much better low temperature flexibility than polyvinylidene chloride films.

Heat Sealing.   Heat sealing of oriented films is generally not very satisfactory since they all shrink, to a greater or lesser degree, below their melting points. Thus, heat seals, when made, tend to shrink and pucker. Satisfactory seals can be made with all of these films by using

TABLE 2.7.   Properties of Oriented Irradiated Polyethylene

	Irradiated Polyethylene	Standard Polyethylene
Yield, sq in./lb	30,000	30,000
Density	.916	.916
Tensile strength psi 22°C	8,000–16,000	1,400–2,500
93°C	1,500–3,000	100–200
Elongation at 22°C	100–200	50–600
Heat sealing range °C	150–300	110–150
% shrink at 96°C	20–55	0–60
Orientation release stress psi at 96°C	100–500	0–10

ultrasonics. Impulse sealing is also satisfactory with most, and dielectric sealing is particularly suited to polyvinylidene chloride type films. Heat seal coatings may also be effective with some oriented films (see Chapter 3).

Orientation Processes. The actual orientation processes which are in use today, or which have been sufficiently reduced to practice to obtain patent coverage, can be separated into two main divisions: *flat sheet* and *tubular*. Within these two general categories, a great variety of mechanical devices has been developed, which impart as little as 10% to as much as 2,000% stretch. Oriented film thicknesses range from .15 to about 60 mils. Little work has so far been reported in biaxial orientation of thicker sections, although this appears to be an area which is ripe for exploitation.

Outside of a handful of general articles on biaxial orientation, very little detailed description of actual processes is available in the literature. However, there is a large number of issued patents, both domestic and foreign, which describe orientation equipment and conditions. The ones which appear most significant and most practical will be briefly discussed in the following section and related, where possible, to the more important commercially available oriented films.

Polyvinylidene Chloride Copolymers. An early patent describing the "Saran" bubble process is illustrated in Figure 2.21.

In this process an 85 : 15 vinylidene–vinyl chloride copolymer, plasticized with 7% of di-(α-phenylethyl) ether is extruded through a circular die orifice at 170°C. This tube is rapidly quenched in a water bath held at 2–7°C in order to amorphize the polymer. To prevent this tacky extruded tube from welding itself shut at the first set of nip rolls,

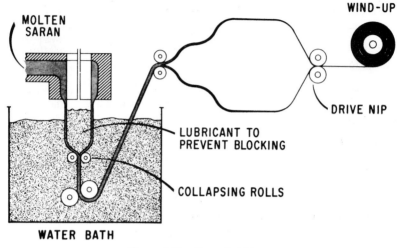

Figure 2.21.   Saran bubble process.

a reservoir of mineral oil is maintained inside this section of the tube. After being flattened at the first set of nip rolls, the tube (2.5 inch diameter, 25 mils thick) passes to a third set of nip rolls outside the cooling bath going at the same speed as the first and second set (10 fpm). Between the third and fourth sets of nip rolls air is introduced into the tube to expand it to about 12 inch diameter. Air pressure is about 1 psi. This room temperature stretch operation introduces the TD orientation. At the same time, the fourth set of nip rolls accelerates the tube by a factor of 3 or 4. Thus, the MD stretch is carried out simul‧ taneously with the TD stretch operation. The expanded tube (12 inch diameter, 2 mils thick) is then collapsed and wound as a tube or flattened and slit to obtain a single sheet at a rate of 75 pounds per hour.

This bubble is self-stabilizing. As the amorphous tube is biaxially stretched, crystallinity as well as orientation is introduced into the film. This increases the tensile strength of the material at a faster rate than the thickness diminishes. At a given internal pressure and tempera- ture, the blown bubble diameter will stabilize where the developed tensile forces just equal the internal pressure. Introduction of more air into the bubble does not increase its diameter, but only the length of the expanded portion. Bubble diameter can be altered by:

(1) Increasing the orientation temperature.
(2) Changing the tubing thickness.
(3) Preheating the tubing before expansion.

(4) Altering the polymer composition or plasticizer content.

(5) Changing the quench conditions to give more or less crystallinity in the cooled extruded tube.

(6) Altering the molecular weight of the resin.

Thus, several processing variables are critical to this particular process, and they must be precisely controlled to obtain a uniform product. The "Saran" film process is shown in Figure 2.22.

The film so obtained is heat shrinkable at a temperature above about 80°C. For many applications a greater degree of heat stability is required and can be obtained, as shown in Figure 2.23.

This process is identical to that shown in Figure 2.21 up to where the inflated bubble is collapsed. Instead of winding onto a roll, the tube is re-expanded under a lower air pressure to its former diameter, led through a cylindrical radiant heating tunnel, collapsed, and wound. This heat treatment, under air pressure restraint, prevents shrinkage or other dimensional change of the film, thus allowing it to retain its beneficial oriented properties. At the same time, crystallite growth is propagated and these crystallites are stable up to the temperature of

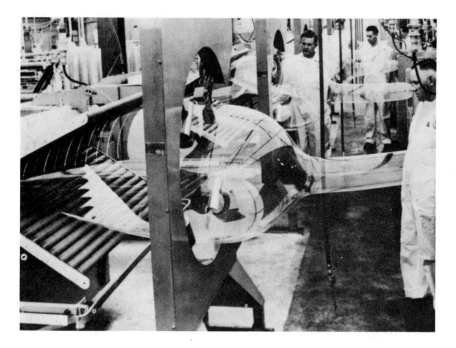

Figure 2.22.   Saran film bubble process in operation. (*Courtesy of The Dow Chemical Co.*)

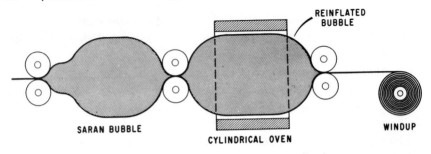

Figure 2.23.   Bubble process for heat stabilization.

treatment. They tend to heat stabilize the film. Examples are shown in Table 2.4.

Polystyrene.   This polymer can be and has been biaxially oriented by a variety of techniques. These are the tentering, bubble, and octagonal stretching processes.

The tentering process is carried out as shown in Figure 2.24. An actual tenter frame is shown in Figure 2.25. A sheet of polystyrene, typically 15 inches wide and 90 mils thick is extruded from a slot die at about 220°C at a rate of 10 fpm. This sheet, under zero tension is passed around two or three polished chill rolls to reduce its temperature to 105–130°C. It next passes through the drafting section where the MD stretch is applied. In the drafting section it is nipped onto one roll

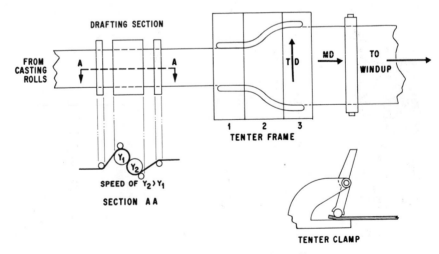

Figure 2.24.   Typical tentering unit.

Figure 2.25.   Tenter frame viewed from delivery end. (*Courtesy of Dalglish Co.*)

at its extruded speed (10 fpm) and onto the next roll going at 30 fpm. This introduces a 300% stretch in the machine direction, and if these two rolls are sufficiently close together, very little diminution in width (necking) occurs. This sheet is then fed directly into the tenter frame. In this frame a series of clips grasp both edges of the sheet. These clips are typically three inches long and are mounted side by side on endless chains. Section 1 is for temperature conditioning of the material and the clips proceed parallel to one another. In Section 2, held at 105–130°C, the tracks diverge and cause the sheet to be stretched in the TD. In Section 3 the biaxially oriented sheet is cooled to below 85°C (Tg); the clips release and a 45 inch wide, 10 mil film is obtained which has been stretched 300% in both directions.

Because of the temperature control problems which are unavoidably associated with this sequential stretching (MD then TD) operation, many modifications of the tenter frame have been proposed. The most frequently suggested improvement is what might be called an accelerating tenterer. Here the temperature conditioned sheet is fed into the tenter frame from a set of constant speed nip rolls, and the TD stretch is put in as before. The MD stretch is put in simultaneously by draw rolls which accelerate the film away from the nip rolls. Thus, both MD and TD orientation are put into the sheet simultaneously. Figure 2.26 illustrates this principle in general.

At first glance, it would appear that this one step process would certainly be more attractive than the two step "conventional" tentering

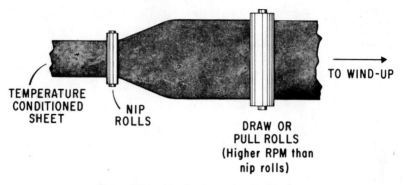

TO WIND-UP

TEMPERATURE
CONDITIONED
SHEET

NIP
ROLLS

DRAW OR
PULL ROLLS
(Higher RPM than
nip rolls)

Figure 2.26.   Idealized accelerating tenterer.

operation described previously. The problem is to develop a practical mechanical system. Most of the patented solutions to this problem rely on one or two mechanisms:

(1) Clips which accelerate along the diverging section.

(2) Stretching sheet which has a bead on each edge so that the edges can ride in diverging slots.

Figure 2.27 apparently combines the best features of accelerating tenter frames developed to date. Here, sheet having a beaded edge is restrained transversely by slots that prevent edge scalloping between clamps, while the bead is accelerated under positive control by grips that accelerate at a controllable rate by using a scissors-like mechanism or a worm gear of decreasing pitch, to which the clamps are attached.

The two main problems associated with a beaded edge operation are:

(1) High trim loss.

(2) High frictional forces encountered in sliding a bead in a slot under the necessary high stretching tensions.

In summarizing the development of simultaneous biaxial tentering type stretch units to date, it appears fair to state that none have the flexibility and degree of control that is possible with the two step tentering process.

The bubble process for making oriented polystyrene film is shown in Figure 2.28. A stream of molten polystyrene at 220°C is forced at a uniform rate through a rotary cooler by a gear pump. Exit temperature is about 140–155°C. Lower temperatures cause problems due to high polymer viscosity. The polymer is then extruded through a tube die, and this tube is expanded around an air bubble to introduce TD orientation. The air pressure required is .14–.33 psi. At the same time,

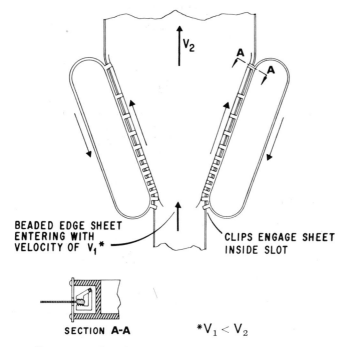

V_2

A

A

BEADED EDGE SHEET
ENTERING WITH
VELOCITY OF V_1*

CLIPS ENGAGE SHEET
INSIDE SLOT

SECTION **A-A**   *$V_1 < V_2$

Figure 2.27.   Simultaneous biaxial stretcher for flat sheet.

the pinch rolls are pulling the film away at a linear rate that is greater than the rate of tube extrusion at the die. This introduces the MD orientation.

This bubble does not have the built-in stabilizing effect, caused by crystallization, that is found in the "Saran" bubble process. If more air is added to the bubble, its diameter expands. That the process is feasible at all is due to two factors. First, as the hot extruded tube is expanding and accelerating downward, it is also cooling. When the thin film reaches 85°C (Tg), its ability to flow or expand further is drastically reduced, and its tensile strength increases sharply. Thus, a falling temperature gradient during biaxial orientation is a requirement for successful air bubble processing of noncrystallizable polymers. Second, the area of greatest instability is near the die, since here the viscosity of the polymer is lowest. The guide ring shown in Figure 2.28 not only keeps the bubble centered, but by rapidly cooling the surface of the tube, provides a hardened skin which further stabilizes the bubble from random motion and promotes better thickness uniformity of film.

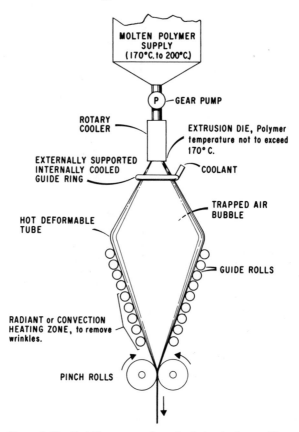

Figure 2.28.   Bubble process for oriented polystyrene film.

The octagonal stretcher, shown in Figure 2.29, illustrates another orienting possibility. In this unit, polystyrene which has been pre-cooled to about 150°C is extruded radially from what might be called a pancake die. Any two points on the film near each other at the die will be found to diverge from one another and to move faster, the further they are displaced from the die. Thus, in essence, the unit is an accelerating tenterer without the complications of any edge gripping mechanisms. During stretching, the sheet is also cooling, and when below Tg, it is slit into eight segments and wound up on eight separate winding stations. The unit has an exceptionally high production capacity, with the added feature that the larger it is, the better it will serve its function. Thus, the unit is well suited to long runs of a particular thickness of material, but gauge changes are more easily accomplished on the bubble and tentering units.

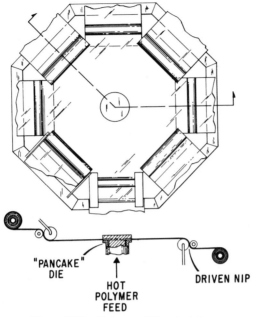

"PANCAKE" DIE

HOT POLYMER FEED

DRIVEN NIP

Figure 2.29.   Octagonal film stretcher.

Polyethylene Terephthalate.   The commercial value of orientation is particularly well illustrated by this polymer. It is made into significant commercial quantities of oriented fiber, heat shrinkable film, and heat stable film. There are no applications for the material in its unoriented form because, if crystalline, it is brittle and opaque, and if amorphous, it is clear but not very tough. When biaxially oriented, however, exceptionally good film properties can be obtained.

Generally, the tentering process is preferred for biaxially orienting this plastic, since at its melting point, 255°C, the polymer has a very low viscosity and, as a result, cannot be readily extruded as a thick tube, cooled, and blown.

A typical stretch operation is as follows:

Amorphous polyethylene terephthalate is extruded at 300°C through a slot die onto a cooling drum held at 65°C to give a sheet 70 mils thick. This quenched amorphous sheet is conducted through a tenter frame where it is stretched 300% in the TD at 90°C. Then still under restraint the sheet is heated to 150°C for 5 seconds. Subsequently the material is stretched 190% in the MD direction between two roll nips rotating at different speeds. The final 8 mil sheet has the properties shown in Table 2.8.

TABLE 2.8. Properties of Oriented Polyethylene Terephthalate

	MD	TD	Unoriented and Amorphous
Tensile strength psi	19,300	17,900	8,000
Tear strength gm/mil	480	507	20
% shrinkage			
(30 min. at 150°C)	+ 5.0	− 2.9*	0
% Elongation	16.5	188	450

* Denotes a net expansion.

A great variation is possible in these physical properties. Film having a 50% shrinkage at 100°C can be obtained by stretching at a low temperature, then quenching without heat stabilization. Also, tensile strengths in excess of 30,000 psi can be obtained by higher stretch ratios at lower temperatures.

Polyvinyl Chloride.   This material and its copolymers (i.e., with monomers such as vinyl acetate), are finding considerable usage as shrink wraps when in biaxially oriented film form. PVC film can be made on a bubble process similar to that used for polystyrene if it is sufficiently plasticized to allow low extrusion temperatures. At extrusion temperatures above about 190°C, too much polymer degradation occurs to allow the trim scrap to be recycled. This process will probably become more popular when heat stabilizers and plasticizers are developed, which have both food approval and a high enough degree of effectiveness to allow scrap recycle.

In the meantime, one of the largest producers is believed to be using the sequence of operations shown in Figure 2.30. PVC is dissolved in a solvent and cast on an endless stainless steel belt. The cast film is then dried and tentered to give a heat shrinkable film. Since low processing temperatures are used throughout, virtually no polymer degradation occurs and the scrap film can thus be recycled. This sequence of dissolving, casting and drying, which includes a solvent recovery process, is obviously more expensive than simple extrusion but is practical because current extrusion technology will not allow scrap recycle.

Polypropylene.   This material can be made into an oriented film which is either shrinkable or heat stable. Either type can be obtained from both the bubble and tentering process.

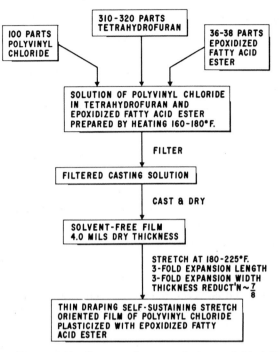

Figure 2.30. Process for manufacture of biaxially oriented polyvinyl chloride film.

In the bubble process, similar to the "Saran" bubble process, a tube is extruded at about 200°C, rapidly quenched to 0–20°C, then reheated to 100–150°C by cylindrical radiant heaters and expanded 2–10 times circumferentially under air pressure while being axially accelerated 2–10 times by the take away nip rolls. Film made in this manner is heat shrinkable at 100–150°C (i.e., will shrink up to 40–50% at 120°C). A shrinkage of less than 3–5% at 120°C can be obtained by reinflating the flattened bubble under lower air pressure, and passing it through tubular heating elements, which heat the film for a few seconds to a temperature near the melting point (i.e., 160°C), then collapsing it.

Tentering lines which are capable of delivering biaxially oriented, heat stabilized, $\frac{1}{2}$ mil, polypropylene films at rates in excess of 500 fpm and widths greater than 100 inches have been designed.

Typical properties of commercial films obtained from bubble and tentering processes have already been shown in Table 2.6. From this limited data sample, it appears that the simultaneous biaxial orientation process (bubble) can produce better balanced film properties.

However, it also appears that the sequential two step orientation process (tentering) can make a higher tensile strength film with a greater degree of heat stability. The property differences, per se, are not sufficiently definite to allow one to say that one process is clearly superior. Similarly, it appears that the capital costs and operating costs of the two types of equipment are comparable. Both processes will likely continue in use.

Irradiated Polyethylene. This film, which is finding a growing market in shrink wrapping, particularly where its good low temperature properties can be used to advantage, is made as shown in Figure 2.31. This process is essentially identical to the original Saran bubble process, with the difference that the extruded and quenched thick wall tube is irradiated before being oriented in bubble form. The irradiation step cross-links the polymer molecules to the extent that the material can still be stretched, but it no longer becomes fluid at its original melting point of 105–110°C. Thus, it retains a relatively high orientation release stress at 100°C, which promotes tight shrink wraps in boiling water. The effects of the added irradiation step are most clearly seen when film prepared identically, but without irradiation, is compared to that made by the foregoing process (see Table 2.7).

Less Common Orientation Techniques. Specialized equipment and processing techniques have been patented for materials which have unusual handling requirements. High density polyethylene cannot be practically amorphized by quenching an extruded melt. Therefore, the bubble process used for saran or polypropylene cannot be used with

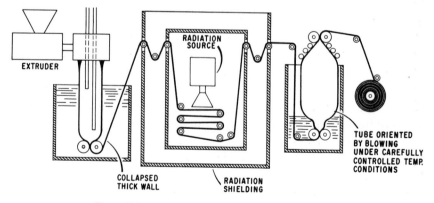

Figure 2.31.   Irradiated polyethylene film process.

linear polyethylene. This material can be oriented, however, by stretching at temperatures very near the melting point, using either the flat sheet or tubular process. Pressure rolling, followed by tentering, has also proved successful with linear polyethylene and with polyoxymethylene polymers.

Low Density Polyethylene. Low density polyethylene films made by the bubble process are generally not regarded as oriented; but they will exhibit shrink characteristics (up to 75%) when heated in an unrestrained manner. Because they do not start shrinking until a temperature near the melting point is reached, they exhibit very low or zero orientation release stress. At these temperatures, the polymer is nearly fluid, since most of the crystallites have melted. Some uses have been developed for these "low shrink energy" films; and since low density polyethylene is the least expensive plastic film resin, some consideration is being given to modified bubble processes which better control the shrink properties of this film. A typical example is shown in Figure 2.32.

The expanding tube temperature is controlled by circulating cooling fluid through a shaped mandrel, which is grit blasted and chrome

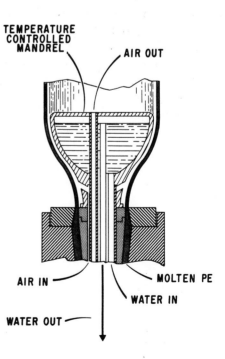

Figure 2.32. Internal cooling of polyethylene bubble for orientation control.

plated to give a microrough, nonsticking surface. This type of equipment gives controlled cooling, which in turn gives more uniform shrink properties to the film. Various mandrel sizes and shapes can further control the final film properties.

Summary. In general, the main features desired in biaxial orientation equipment are:

(1) Capability for introducing "balanced" or desired degree of "unbalanced" orientation properties into a film or sheet.

(2) Ability to obtain maximum levels of orientation when desired.

(3) The MD and TD stretch ratio should be independently variable at will.

(4) Precise temperature control in the stretch zones and uniformity of temperature in the polymer feed.

(5) The apparatus should be capable of giving high rates of stretch and high or low stretch ratios.

(6) Scrap losses, particularly edge trim, should be kept to a minimum.

The single or double bubble process embodies many of these desirable features; however, the two-step tentering process appears to have greater flexibility. Thus, while it is believed that the two-step tentering process is the most versatile biaxial orienting procedure, the preferred process for a particular polymer still has to be carefully chosen, for in many instances the bubble process may give a good enough product and use less complicated equipment. In other cases, both bubble and tenterer may be used without either having sufficiently clearly defined advantages to be proven superior. Finally, to date, no processes have been developed which appear likely to obsolete either the bubble or the tenter process.

More detailed information may be found in the section titled Biaxial Orientation, by W. R. R. Park and Jo Conrad, in the "Encyclopedia of Polymer Science and Technology," Volume 2, pp. 339–373.

THREE

coated plastic films

W. R. R. PARK

Coatings are used to enhance the properties of many plastic films. These coatings are generally less than .001 inch in thickness, are applied to one or both sides, and are deposited from lacquers, latexes, aqueous solutions, and dispersions. The major reasons for applying coatings are to:

(1) Modify the heat sealing behavior.

(2) Improve the barrier properties.

(3) Change the handling characteristics (slip, scratch resistance, block, static, fogging, etc.).

In certain circumstances, the application of highly specialized and usually thicker coatings leads to functional products from plastic films. Examples of such are photographic films where light sensitive emulsions are applied to plastic film substrates (cellulose acetate, polyester, and polystyrene), plastic tracing papers using polyester film for its toughness and dimensional stability, recording and control tapes based on cellulose acetate and polyester, wood grain printed films for lamination to wall paneling, pressure sensitive tapes, decorative decals, etc. The utility of these products depends on highly developed coatings, whose formulation is beyond the scope of this book.

Coated Cellophanes. While cellophane is not, strictly speaking, a plastic film, it exhibits many plasticlike properties. It is clear, flexible, and tough. In terms of volume, it is by far the most important coated film available today. The total production of all other coated plastic films does not yet approach the yearly tonnage sales of cellophane. Thus, cellophane is likely to remain a leader in this area for a number of years.

This position of preeminence did not just happen. It is the result of years of continuing research and development effort directed towards improving properties and functionality. Today cellophane is a very broad term encompassing well over a hundred distinct varieties of film. Each type has properties which are custom-made to match, as nearly as possible, the packaging requirements of particular products.

Properties attainable from various grades of cellophane range from very low to high gas and moisture vapor permeability, zero to high strength heat seals, one side coated film which is sealable to either coated or uncoated side, etc. Some grades are produced in as many as ten colors. Flame resistant grades are also available. Recent modifications on the substrate itself have improved its toughness sufficiently so that a 10–20% decrease in thickness could be made with no sacrifice in strength.

In a number of ways, coatings and cellophane substrates complement each other almost ideally. Plain cellophane has very limited markets, since it cannot be heat sealed. It does not melt. This property makes it an excellent substrate for the application of heat sealable coatings. It means not only that coatings can be dried at high temperatures, but also that they can be heat sealed over a broad temperature range without seriously affecting the properties of the base film. This becomes a real advantage when, for instance, an overwrapping machine jams while a wrapped package is in contact with the heat seal bars. The overheated film does not melt, flow, and gum up the machinery, as occurs if the film is truly thermoplastic. Also, uncoated cellophane is highly moisture sensitive, and, if allowed to age under low humidity conditions, it embrittles rapidly with some shrinkage. Under high humidity conditions it absorbs water rapidly and softens with swelling. The application of barrier coatings improves the dimensional stability of cellophanes to changing humidity conditions. This lack of good dimensional stability under varying humidity conditions is the only major drawback of cellophane films. Its effect is minimized by processing, storing, and using under conditions which are held as close as practical to 40–50% R.H. at 75°F. Unfortunately, it is not possible to control the environment of the wrapped package after it leaves the fabricator, and this can still lead to aging problems, even with the physical property improvements obtained by coating.

Cellophane manufacturers attempt to compensate for these effects by altering the water and softener content of their films on a seasonal basis. These films generally contain 5–10% of water and 8–25% of plasticizers or softeners, which are usually ethylene glycol, propylene glycol, glycerol, and polyols, or mixtures of these materials. During the winter, when lower humidity conditions prevail, a higher plasticizer content helps retain the pliability of cellophane.

Coatings for Cellophane.   There are three distinct chemical types of cellophane coatings. In historical order of development these are nitrocellulose, polyvinylidene chloride, and vinyl. They have some common properties. They can all be formulated to give heat sealable coatings, and all are clear, have high gloss, excellent printability, easy machineability, good slip, and improved barrier properties compared with those of uncoated cellophane. Each type also has specific advantages. The nitrocellulose coatings are the least expensive and can be applied at the highest rates, since solvent removal is more readily accomplished through this relatively poor barrier material. These coatings provide good barrier properties to cellophane as long as it is not sharply creased, but these coatings tend to be brittle and to fracture at creases or wherever it is roughly handled. The many types of nitrocellulose coated cellophanes still account for more than half of all cellophane sold.

Polyvinylidene chloride coatings provide better gas and moisture barrier properties, as well as greater flexibility. They also have superior grease and oil resistance properties. These polymeric coatings are not brittle and maintain their integrity even over sharp creases, since they are more elastic than nitrocellulose types. Usually, where the best barrier type of protection is needed in an overwrap, the polyvinylidene chloride type of coated cellophane will be used. Each year, more of this type of cellophane is used in preference to the nitrocellulose coated varieties. This is economically feasible because, while these Saran type coatings are initially more expensive, it is becoming practical to use thinner polyvinylidene chloride coatings (.05 mil) to give barriers and heat seal strengths equivalent to thicker (.10 mil) nitrocellulose coatings. Improved polyvinylidene chloride resins and improvements in coating technology have made this possible. The best barrier cellophanes still use the thicker polyvinylidene chloride coating, and these are demonstrably superior to nitrocellulose coatings.

Since polyvinylidene chloride resins have such superior barrier properties, a great deal of difficulty was initially encountered in their use
as lacquer coatings for cellophane. It is extremely difficult to remove the
last traces of solvent from the coatings. Any residual solvent leads to
odor problems, which are not tolerable in food packaging, even though
the levels may be well below anything that might be considered toxic.
This barrier characteristic of polyvinylidene chloride coatings also
interferes with rehumidification of the cellophane substrate after the
coating has been adequately dried. However, these problems have been
largely overcome, and cellophane is now coated with polyvinylidene
chloride lacquer at speeds approaching those attainable with nitrocellulose lacquers. Most domestic polyvinylidene chloride coating is
made from lacquer, but in Europe the polyvinylidene chloride latex
coating approach is favored. Neither is clearly superior.

The third main coating type, introduced by American Viscose Corporation in 1963, consists of a vinyl copolymer which is applied from
a lacquer system. This coating has barrier properties and prices intermediate between polyvinylidene chloride and nitrocellulose coatings
and, thus, serves to complete the spectrum of properties available in
coated cellophanes. In turn, this means that a packager may now be
able to obtain adequate properties at a somewhat reduced cost.

These three coating types, nitrocellulose, polyvinylidene chloride, and
vinyl are available in a large number of grades. Polyvinylidene chloride
coated cellophanes are made in at least ten grades ranging in thickness
from .8–1.7 mil. Nitrocellulose coated cellophanes are available in heat
sealing grades, moistureproof, and with limited moistureproofness.
Some grades are designed specifically to be extrusion coated with polyethylene, and others can be purchased with polyethylene already laminated to cellophane. Other grades are coated on one side only to increase
their gas transmission rates without causing serious loss in moisture
vapor transmission rates. These types are particularly valuable for
packaging fresh red meat where an oxygen supply is necessary to keep
the red bloom on the meat and, at the same time, to prevent undue
moisture loss. The uncoated side of the film is exposed to the moist meat
and, as the film absorbs moisture, it becomes more permeable to oxygen
and other gases. Figure 3.1 illustrates this behavior. The film so used
essentially equilibrates at 100% relative humidity. Other varieties of
cellophane have special nonfogging or heat seal bar release properties.

The variability of transmission properties which are attainable with
the three main types of film is most practically demonstrated when

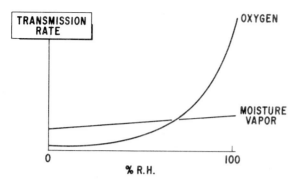

Figure 3.1.   Effect of humidity on gas and moisture transmission rate*.

*One side coated cellophane.

the films are used identically as overwraps for materials which tend to either gain or lose water. A few examples are shown in Table 3.1. Actual percent weight gains or losses of a packaged item will depend on many factors, but typical performances are shown in Table 3.2.

Table 3.3 lists a few of the popular grades of cellophane that are available from the three domestic manufacturers and which have comparable properties. Table 3.4 lists the selected principal uses of cellophanes using the duPont code designations.

Coated Paper.   Paper may be considered a substrate comparable to plain cellophane in many ways. It is not heat sealable, has poor barrier characteristics, and is moisture sensitive. In addition, it is opaque and has a relatively rough, porous surface. These properties can be sufficiently upgraded by applying various types of coatings, so that the coated papers acquire many of the desirable functional properties of homogeneous plastic films. Simple lacquer coatings of the nitrocellulose type are often used to give a glossy, scuff resistant finish to many different types of papers for a decorative effect.

The main reason for coating paper then is obvious. Paper can be converted into a functional, heat sealable, barrier type of packaging film at lower overall cost than is possible with any other substrate. Again, like cellophane, paper is well suited to coating operations, since it is flat and has high heat resistance, which allows high temperatures to be used for drying of coatings. A wide range of heat sealing temperatures may be used on coated paper without causing degradation of the substrate.

TABLE 3.1. Weight Gains of Cellophane Wrapped Packages*

Coating Type	75°F. 11% R.H.		90°F. 45% R.H.		40°F. 93% R.H.		75°F. 93% R.H.	
	1 Week	2 Weeks	1 Week	2 Weeks	1 Week	2 Weeks	1 Week	2 Weeks
	Donuts		Donuts					
Nitrocellulose	−4.85	−9.28	−1.88	−3.56				
Vinyl	−2.45	−5.63	−1.48	−2.84				
Polyvinylidene chloride	−1.00**	−1.74	−1.00	−1.68				
	Bread		Bread					
Nitrocellulose	−3.24	−6.50	−1.93	−3.56				
Vinyl	−1.25	−2.94	−1.10	−2.74				
Polyvinylidene chloride	−1.00	−1.95	−1.00	−2.00				
					Potato Chips		Potato Chips	
Nitrocellulose					5.68	10.40	4.35	6.84
Vinyl					2.85	5.80	2.56	3.86
Polyvinylidene chloride					1.00	1.78	1.00	1.68
					Cookies		Cookies	
Nitrocellulose					1.08	1.80	2.25	4.24
Vinyl					0.82	1.51	1.55	2.81
Polyvinylidene chloride					1.00	1.48	1.00	1.53

* A negative number denotes weight loss.
** Polyvinylidene chloride coated cellophane is considered unity, and the other films are compared to its effectiveness on a ratio basis.

TABLE 3.2.   % Weight Loss of Cellophane Wrapped Packages

Coating type	86°F at 32% R.H. for 7 days	75°F at 93% R.H. for 7 days
	Pound Cake	Chocolate Chip Cookies
Nitrocellulose	7.0–8.0	3.5
Vinyl	4–5	1.9
Polyvinylidene chloride	1.5–2.0	.2

TABLE 3.3.   Common Cellophane Types

General Type	duPont	Avisco	Olin
Plain, nonmoistureproof	PD	P-1	—
Nitrocellulose coated, heat sealable, limited	LSD	DS	LST
moistureproofness	LSAD	DSB	LSAT
Nitrocellulose coated, moistureproof, heat	MASD-80	MSBO	MSAT-80,
sealable for fresh meats	88, 90	AMO	OF-16
Nitrocellulose coated,	MSB-52	MS-2	MST-52
moistureproof,	MSD-53	MS-3	MST-53
heat sealing	MSD-54	MS-4	MST-54
	MSD-58	MS-8	MST-58
	MSAD-86	MSB-6	MSAT-86
	MSAD-87	MSB-7	MSAT-87
Nitrocellulose coated,	MD-31	M-1	MT-31
moistureproof, nonheat	MD-32	M-2	—
sealing for tobacco	MD-35	M-5	MT-35
	MAD-2	MB	—
Polyvinylidene chloride	K-201	RS-1	V
coated, moistureproof,	K-202	RS-2	V
heat sealable	K-203*		
Vinyl coated, moistureproof, heat sealable	—	R-18	—
Extrusion coating film	K-204	—	—
	MSAD-10		
	K-205 Lam.**		

* Nonfogging.
** Made of K-201 extrusion coated one side with ¼ mil polyethylene.

Unlike cellophane, paper has a rough and porous surface, however, which causes coating problems. Since papers are more or less absorbent, they require a primer treatment of some sort to close the pores before the functional coating, usually polyvinylidene chloride is applied. The most common techniques in use for priming paper are:

(1) Clay coating using a styrene–butadiene latex binder.

(2) Extrusion coating with a thin layer of polyethylene.

(3) Using multiple coats of polyvinylidene chloride latex or lacquer.

Each method has advantages. The clay coating technique is well worked out and is commonly used to improve the surface smoothness and printability of paper. A typical coating formulation would contain 100 parts of coating clay, 20 parts of starch, and 20 parts of styrene butadiene latex, all on a dry weight basis. This coating, when applied at about six pounds per ream, is quite effective in preventing subsequently applied coatings from being absorbed into the paper substrate. Such primers can be applied by air knife or size press techniques. This holdout coating is, however, not perfect, and while much less porous than plain paper, it will usually require a double coating to ensure freedom from pinholes.

TABLE 3.4.   Types* of Cellophane most Commonly Used for Principal Applications

Bread, sweet doughs, cakes and baked goods	K-201, MSD-60
Candy twist wraps	MD-35
Caramel overwrap	MD-36
Cigarettes	MD-31
Cigars	MSD-58-T, MD-32
Moist Produce Items	MSAD-86
Frozen foods	K-203, MSAD-87
Fresh meats	MSAD-80, 88, 90
Processed meats, fresh fruits and vegetables	LSAD
Carton Overwrap	MSD-52, 54
Bags, direct wraps and overwraps of superior durability	K-201, K-203, K-207
Bags of good durability	MSD-53
Heavy or hard items such as candy, macaroni	K-202 (11,600 sq in./lb)

* duPont designations.

Probably the most certain method of closing the pores in the paper surface is the application of a thin extrusion coating of polyethylene. High quality papers can be perfectly sealed with as little as $\frac{1}{4}$ mil of polyethylene, although $\frac{1}{2}$–1 mil coatings are more commonly used. Using this surface sealing method, single topcoats of $\frac{1}{10}$–$\frac{3}{10}$ mil of polyvinylidene chloride can be applied with good assurance of freedom from pinholes due to coating absorption by the substrate.

While extrusion coating is the most certain sealing method, it has the drawbacks of requiring specialized equipment which not all paper converters possess. Also, polyvinylidene chloride does not adhere readily to polyethylene. Since heat seal strength of coated papers may depend largely on coating adhesion, polyethylene coated paper has to be corona treated before coating. To obtain the highest level of adhesion, this stock has to be primed after corona treating. The types of primers used most commonly are discussed in detail in Chapter 6 under Extrusion Coating. Thus, while extrusion coating to seal the surface is the surest technique, it is also the most complex and perhaps the most expensive method.

Sealing the surface with a prime coat which has the same composition as the topcoat has several desirable features. First, since the prime coat penetrates as it seals the surface, it adheres strongly due to mechanical interlocking. Secondly, adhesion of the topcoat is no problem since it has the same composition as the primer. This method does require at least a double and often a triple coating to be certain of obtaining a pinholefree structure.

All three priming methods have utility, and the choice of technique depends more on availability of various types of coating equipment than on the outstanding merits of any single technique.

Coatings in Use on Paper.   The polyvinylidene chloride polymers are the only types, other than waxes, that find appreciable usage in functional paper coatings. They provide moisture and gas barrier, excellent grease and oil resistance, heat sealability, gloss, and flavor retention properties.

To date, polyvinylidene chloride latexes have been more widely used than polyvinylidene chloride lacquers. The reason is an economic, not technological one, since nearly comparable properties can be obtained from the two systems. The use of lacquers, however, requires solvent recovery units to reduce costs, while latexes have no solvent recovery problem. If sufficiently large markets should develop for a few types of polyvinylidene chloride coated paper or glassine, the trend might reverse in favor of lacquers. This could justify the construction of sophisticated coating and solvent recovery equipment similar to that used for cellophane coating and could make lacquer coated paper competitive with latex coated paper. Lacquer coating does have the advantages of simpler control, fewer cleanup problems, and greater reproducibility. These coatings will invariably have somewhat better moisture vapor transmission rates (MVTR) and water resistance properties than are attainable from a latex of the same chemical composition, since latexes, of necessity, will contain some quantity of wetting agent which remains in the dried film and makes it more or less water sensitive. Gas transmission properties are comparable for the two coating systems. The improved transmission rates that are obtained from polyvinylidene chloride lacquer coatings on polyethylene coated paper and glassine are shown in Table 3.5.

TABLE 3.5. Effect of "Saran" F-220* Coatings on Transmission Properties

Coating thickness	WVTR†	O_2TR††
PE coated paper** control	.94	114
plus .04 mil "Saran" F-220	.82	.9
plus .06 mil "Saran" F-220	.69	.5
Glassine control	>200	1,000
plus .06 mil "Saran" F-220	3.8	13
plus .20 mil "Saran" F-220 (2 coats)	.7	> .3

* Dow Saran Resin F-220 applied from 20% acetone solution.
** 1 mil PE coating.
† gm/100 sq in./24 hr at 100°F + 95% R.H.
†† cc/100 sq in./24 hr/atm at 25°C.

It can be seen that polyethylene primed paper allows the use of a much thinner single coat of lacquer to obtain good barrier properties, and that a double coating thickness is necessary on glassine to ensure pinhole-free properties. Also, it is seen that the use of polyethylene primed paper as a substrate can largely overcome the MVTR deficiency of polyvinylidene chloride latex coating, since polyethylene is a good moisture barrier in itself.

The domestic use of saran latex coatings has lagged behind European developments in this area. It appears that while polyethylene extrusion coating technology for paper was being perfected in the United States, the Europeans were concentrating on developing good polyvinylidene chloride latex coatings for paper. Neither approach solves all the problems inherent in paper coatings, and now both techniques are being used worldwide to upgrade paper properties. A comparison of properties that can be obtained by the two coating systems is shown in Table 3.6.

The most serious drawback of saran latex coated paper is its poor crease resistance. This factor has limited the use of such papers almost exclusively to pouch pack constructions. These are finding use in a number of areas such as portion packs for suntan cream, instant chocolate, coffee, cream, orange juice, wash and dry tissues, jello, dried milk, dried soup, band aids, deodorants, etc., where good barrier and grease resistance are needed at a lower cost than can be realized using aluminum foil. Coffee bags, detergent boxes and foil-fiber oil cans also are beginning to use polyvinylidene chloride coated papers.

TABLE 3.6. Properties of Polyethylene and Polyvinylidene Chloride Coated Paper

Polyethylene Coating	Polyvinylidene Chloride Coating
Strong heat seals	Strong heat seals
Excellent flexibility	Comparatively poor crease resistance
Single coating operation	At least double coating
Good MVTR	Excellent MVTR
Poor GTR	Excellent GTR
Poor grease resistance	Excellent grease resistance
Low gloss	High gloss
.5–2.0 mils needed	.2–.5 mils usually adequate
Remains colorless	Slight yellowing tendency

Over the long range, it appears likely that polyvinylidene chloride latex (or lacquer) coatings on polyethylene primed paper will find increased utility. This construction gives the best possible combination of properties. A thin latex coating over polyethylene primed paper will give barrier properties equivalent to those obtained from 3–5 times the amount of the same polyvinylidene chloride latex applied to unprimed paper. Secondly, and perhaps of more importance, the thinner polyvinylidene chloride coating is more flexible and has much better crease resistance, which may allow these coated papers to find use in areas other than flat pouch packs.

Coated Polyester Films. Plain polyester films suffer from problems similar to those of plain cellophane. They cannot be readily heat sealed by conventional methods. Polyester films do melt, but because they are biaxially oriented, they shrink extensively at temperatures well below their melting point. Thermoplastic coatings which melt below the shrink temperature of the film effectively overcome this heat sealing limitation.

To date, only polyvinylidene chloride type materials have found extensive use in polyester coatings, and duPont is the only domestic supplier. A number of converters also coat polyester films on a custom basis when special grades of film are needed. The coatings may be either latex or lacquer type, since polyester films are not particularly sensitive to either water or solvents.

TABLE 3.7. Properties of Polyvinylidene Chloride Coated "Mylar" Polyester Films

DuPont Designation	Substrate Thickness (mils)	Coating Thickness (mils)	Sq In. per Lb	MVTR gm/100 sq in./24 hr At 95% R.H.	O₂TR c.c./100 sq in./24 hr 1 atm	Heat Seal Strength gm/in.	Principal Uses
M-22	.50	.10 per side	27,600	<.5	<.5		Bag making.
M-23	.7	.10 per side	20,500				Bundling and overwrapping.
	.50	.10 per side	27,600				
M-24*	.50	.10 one side only	32,700	.8	.4**	120°C–0	For laminating or extrusion coating on coated side—used for vacuum or inert gas packaging.
	.75	.10 one side only	23,400			135°C–242	
						150°C–292	
M-25	.50	.10 one side only	32,700				For laminating or extrusion coating on coated side. Substrate has superior forming characteristics.
	.75	.10 one side only	23,400				
M-26	.50	.20 per side	21,600	Good	Good	>300	Extra heavy coating to give strongest crimp seals which can withstand dump loading. For form and fill bag equipment.

* Block free at 60°C.
** Virtually unaffected by % R.H.

The properties of the readily available types are summarized in Table 3.7. In many respects, these coated, heat sealable polyester films represent the best balance of desirable packaging properties that are available in any film. They are flexible and tough from − 80°F to over 300°F, are unaffected by boiling water, show no dimensional instability, are puncture and tear resistant, sparkling clear, have high tensile and impact strength. On an area basis they cost about $2\frac{1}{2}$–4 times as much as the thickest polyvinylidene chloride coated cellophane.

Coated Oriented Polypropylene Films. The only currently available heat sealable films that appear likely to be able to compete for existing cellophane markets are the coated oriented polypropylene films. They have the potential of being priced comparably on an area basis and have some definite advantages over coated cellophanes. First, they age better and do not change dimensionally with changing ambient humidity conditions. Secondly, they have higher strength per unit thickness and, thirdly, they have as good or better gloss and transparency. They will have to be handled somewhat more carefully by packagers, however, since like all other oriented thermoplastic films, if overheated, they shrink extensively and will melt. A summary of properties of these types of films is found in Table 3.8.

It has been demonstrated that these films can be run interchangeably with cellophane on some overwrap machines with no machinery modifications, and on others with a minimum of mechanical changes being needed. See Figure 3.2 for examples.

Latexes are the preferred coating system for polypropylene film, since it is solvent sensitive to a much greater degree than polyester films. Usually a primer coating of some type is required to develop the best adhesion levels, which in turn yield the greatest heat seal strengths.

Coated Polystyrene Film. Oriented polystyrene film also shrinks before it melts and, thus, cannot be satisfactorily heat sealed. Since this plastic is sensitive to almost all solvents except alcohols, any alcohol soluble lacquer coatings can be used. Such materials are polyvinyl acetal, polyvinyl butyral, and ethyl cellulose. All of these can be formulated to give heat sealable coatings for polystyrene film, but all require the use of an adhesive primer, since they will not adhere directly to polystyrene. One useful primer is 60 : 40 styrene-butadiene latex. Any of the available types of latex coatings can be used on polystyrene film, since it is not water sensitive, and heat sealable polyvinyl acetate

TABLE 3.8.† Properties of Coated, Oriented Polypropylene Films

Trade Name	Manufacturer	Composition	Substrate Thickness (mils)	Coating Thickness (mils)	Heat Seal* (gm/in.)	MVTR gm/100 sq in./24 hr 100°F–90% R.H.	O_2TR	Tensile (psi)	Elongation (%)	Block Resistance	Slip
Olefane C-TD-12	Avisun	Polyvinylidene chloride	.60	~.1 per side	200	.4	6–8	MD 10,000 TD 30,000	MD 440 TD 30	Good	—
Olefane C-TD-11	—	PVAc	.60	~.1 per side	200	.4	140	Same	—	Fair	—
CelKor	Kordite	PVAc	.60	~.1 per side	200	.4	75	MD 25,000 TD 30,000	MD 90	Good	.20
Clysar	DuPont	Polyvinylidene chloride	1.00	~.1 per side	up to 450 at 150°C	—	—	—	—	Good	.22
Propathene C	I.C.I.	Polyvinylidene chloride	.50	.075 per side	200–300	.3	0.6	MD 20,000 TD 20,000	50–75	Good	.25–.30
Dynafilm	U.S.I.	PVAc	.60	~.1 per side	200	.4	100	MD 10,000 TD 27,000	MD 360	Good	.2–.3
	Hercules	Polyvinylidene chloride	.5–1.0	~.1 per side	200–300	.3–.4	1.0	MD 22,000 TD 23,000	50–60	Good	.2

* Heat seal range may be as wide as 90–150°C.

† Dow Chemical Company data supplemented by manufacturers bulletins.

Figure 3.2. 320 celKor film for general machine overwrap. Developed for general machine overwrap of confectionery and pharmaceuticals, staples, tobacco products. New film introduced 4/20/64, offers exceptional cold temperature strength (−30°F) and indefinite shelf life properties. Operates on all existing cellophane packaging machines, without need for conversion. Film slides and seals on hot bare metal. Machine operators require no special training. Transparency, sparkle and feel of 320 celKor are equal to cellophane. (*Courtesy of Kordite Corp., Films Div.*)

latex coatings have been developed. Heat sealable, barrier coatings using polyvinylidene chloride latexes applied over adhesive primers have also been developed for polystyrene film. None of these coated films have found commercial utility, largely because they do not offer significant improvements in performance properties, or cost over other already established heat sealable films.

Polyvinylidene chloride latex coatings may still find utility in this area when they are used to modify the barrier properties of oriented polystyrene sheet (3–20 mils). This sheet finds widespread use in formed food containers of various types. Some of these containers could be significantly improved by the application of moisture and gas barrier type coatings.

Other simple coatings have found utility on polystyrene film. Antifog coated film is prepared by the application of dilute solutions of various wetting agents to the surface. Scratch resistant coatings can be made from cellulose acetate lacquers or acrylate latexes.

Coated Polyethylene Films. The properties of polyethylene films may be improved by coating. In particular, the grease and oil resistance of polyethylene can be significantly upgraded through the application of polyvinylidene chloride coatings. Such coatings also markedly improve the barrier properties. The resulting coated film has found few markets due largely to the difficulty of heat sealing the coating without causing the substrate to melt at the same time. When these same coatings are applied to medium or high density polyethylene films, which have higher melting points and will allow a wider heat sealing temperature range, markets may develop. The higher density polyethylenes are also stiffer and should give a more handleable coated film than the low density polymer. Whether such coated films can compete with coated oriented polypropylene films remains to be seen.

One highly suitable application has developed for polyvinylidene chloride coated low density polyethylene film. One coated sheet is embossed with small blisters. This sheet is then heat sealed to another flat film of polyvinylidene chloride coated polyethylene. The resulting construction (Figure 3.3) has bubbles of trapped air that remain as bubbles because of the impermeability of the polyvinylidene chloride coating. The softness of the substrate is an advantage here, since the laminate has found utility as cushion packing, which has proven superior to existing types of packing used to protect delicate instruments during shipping.

Typical Coating Formulations. Coating formulations are, of course, carefully tailored with respect to both the substrate and

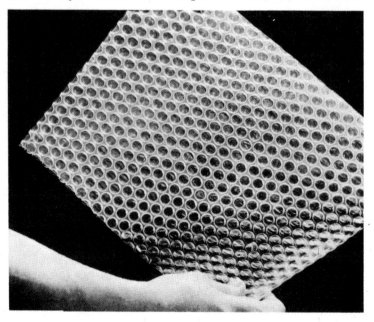

Figure 3.3.   Saran coated polyethylene film converted into novel cushion packaging material. (*Courtesy of Sealed Air Corp.*)

subsequent use of the coated film, but, in general, the coating components are the same regardless of the substrate.

Nitrocellulose coatings for cellophane (or paper) can be made to have
better barrier properties and poorer crease resistance by increasing the
wax content. Heat seal strength can be increased by the use of higher
plasticizer content. This usually detracts from the barrier and slip
properties. Slip properties may be improved by adding more talc or
zinc stearate to the coating at the expense of clarity and gloss. Adhesion-
improving additives may detract from the heat seal strengths. Higher
resin contents can lower the initial heat sealing temperature but may
cause blocking problems.

Thus, the attainment of a "balanced" coating formulation for a given
application will often require an extensive and intensive development
and screening program and will involve many compromises. Judging
from the number of distinct types of coated cellophanes that have been
developed, the trend in film coatings will continue to be towards

Nitrocellulose Coatings.   Typical components are shown below.

Component	% By Wt.	Comments
Nitrocellulose	50	Available in a range of molecular weights. Usually low molecular weight resins give higher solids content at lower viscosities. Used for its film forming qualities, strength and toughness.
Plasticizer	20	Many may be used. Dicyclohexyl phthalate, tricresyl phosphate, castor oil, dioctyl phthalate are typical. Usually two or more are used in any given coating. Used to soften the nitrocellulose.
Resin	15	These may be vinyls, alkyds, rosin derivatives, ester gums, etc., and range in properties from very soft to very hard. Several are often used in a single formulation; used to lower cost and modify hardness and adhesion properties.
Wax	10	May be paraffin, microcrystalline, vegetable or animal waxes such as carnauba or beeswax. Used to improve slip, block resistance and barrier properties. Often require heated solvents to keep in solution.
Slip agents Antistatic agents Antisticking agents Viscosity modifiers Light stabilizers Flow agents Defoamers, etc.	5	Dispersions of talc, zinc stearate, etc. May be wetting agents which bloom to surface. Silicones prevent sticking to heat seal bars. Many other less obvious but still functional additives may be included in this last 5%.
	100	

tailor-making coated films for specific applications. This is actually one of the main strong points in favor of coated films. Properties of the finished film, such as heat seal, barrier, slip, etc., can be modified by altering the coating formulation, which generally comprises no more than 25% of the finished film weight. To obtain the same properties solely by altering the substrate is often not possible.

The solvents used for such lacquers are usually mixtures comprised of so-called diluents, latent solvents, and active solvents. A typical mixture might include:

Ethanol 10	Ethyl Acetate 10
Butanol 10	Butyl Acetate 20
Toluene 50	

The objective is to find the least expensive solvent combination which will hold all coating components in solution (often at elevated temperatures) and which will evaporate at the right rate to prevent development of surface defects. Different drying conditions often require altered solvent ratios. Nitrocellulose lacquers are seldom used at total solids content greater than 15–20% by weight.

Polyvinylidene Chloride Lacquers. Polyvinylidene chloride lacquers generally do not require as high a percentage of formulants, since the resin itself can be tough, film-forming, and relatively heat sealable. The coating formulation will vary with regard to initial heat seal temperature, coating extensibility, slip properties, etc., to ensure that the coating properties are as compatible as possible with those of the

Polyvinylidene Chloride Coating Components

Component	% By Wt.	Comments
Polyvinylidene chloride	85	Will usually contain 80–95% vinylidene chloride plus at least one other monomer of which acrylonitrile, vinyl chloride, ethyl acrylate, and butyl acrylate are the most common. Acids such as maleic or itaconic may be copolymerized to provide better adhesion properties.
Plasticizer	10	Added to increase flexibility, lower heat seal temperature. Phthalate, adipate and citrate esters are typical.
Wax	3	Improve block and slip properties—carnauba, paraffin, and microcrystalline types used.
Destaticizers	2	Usually wetting agents.
Slip agents		Talc or other inorganic pigments.
UV absorbers		
	———	
	100	

substrate, be it cellophane, polyester, polypropylene, paper or polyethylene.

The solvent systems required to dissolve polyvinylidene chloride resins vary with the resin composition. At vinylidene chloride concentrations of 80% or less, acetone will often serve. As the vinylidene chloride content increases above 90%, these resins require stronger solvents such as tetrahydrofuran to make low viscosity, high solids (20% maximum) solutions. Since many lacquer compositions contain wax, it is often necessary to heat the solvents to 70–80°C to keep the wax in solution. This has a double benefit. The solution viscosity decreases with increasing temperature, and weaker solvents can be used. Mixtures of methyl ethyl ketone and toluene have quite good solvent powers when hot and are much less expensive than solvents such as tetrahydrofuran.

Since polyvinylidene chloride is an excellent barrier not only towards gases and water but also towards solvents, difficulties can be encountered in removing the last traces of solvents from lacquer coatings. As a result, drying systems either have to be operated at lower speeds or made longer when polyvinylidene chloride coatings are being applied to a substrate. Any solvent retention is objectionable from an odor point of view. Also, even very small quantities of residual solvent will cause a serious degradation in the barrier and blocking properties of the coating.

Polyvinylidene Chloride Latexes. Polyvinylidene chloride latexes, which are dispersions of discrete polymer particles (200–2,000 Å diameter) in water, have different handling properties from those of polyvinylidene chloride lacquers. A comparison of these two types of coatings follows:

Polyvinylidene Chloride Latex	*Polyvinylidene Chloride Lacquer*
Can be used at 40–60% solids.	Used at 10–20% solids.
Water is solvent.	Flammable solvents must be used.
No solvent recovery system needed.	Solvent recovery system essential for economical coating operation.
Coating unit need not be explosion proof.	Coating machinery must be explosion proof.
Formulating costs are comparable	
Are used at room temperatures.	Generally must be heated.
Must be protected from freezing.	No temperature stability problems.
Can have shear stability problems.	No shear stability problems.
High vinylidene chloride content does not affect viscosity.	High vinylidene chloride content causes higher viscosities.
Low viscosity.	High viscosity.

Contains wetting agents which remain in film and adversely affect MVTR in proportion to their content.	No wetting agents remain in lacquer.
	Have comparable GTR's
Relatively easy to dry.	Difficult to remove last solvent traces.
Continuous coatings less than .05 mil thick are possible with both systems	
pH control critical.	pH control noncritical.
Surface tension generally must be lowered to get good wetting.	Lacquer solvents already have low surface tension.

Formulation of polyvinylidene chloride latex coatings differs from that of lacquers in that most formulants must be emulsified or dispersed in water before being added to the coating. The same general types of additives, plasticizers, waxes, wetting agents, slip agents, defoamers, etc., can be used once techniques are worked out to disperse them in water.

Generally, the choice between using polyvinylidene chloride latex or lacquer coatings depends on factors other than the properties attainable with the two systems, since they are very comparable. Latexes are preferred for polypropylene film coating, since the substrate is solvent sensitive. Both latex and lacquer coatings are used on cellophane, but lacquer seems preferred, since the substrate is somewhat moisture sensitive. Also, cellophane manufacturers already had much lacquer coating experience and solvent recovery know-how before polyvinylidene chloride coatings were developed, and they could more easily handle lacquers. Latexes are currently preferred for paper coating, even though the substrate is moisture sensitive, because sufficiently large markets for polyvinylidene chloride coated paper have not yet developed to justify the purchase of more complex lacquer coating equipment.

Polyvinyl Acetate Latexes.   These materials can also be formulated to give heat sealable coatings, but they have essentially no barrier properties. Therefore, they will never find much use in cellophane coatings, where the substrate needs moisture protection, but can be used to confer heat sealing properties on films such as polypropylene, polyethylene, polystyrene, polyesters, or cellulose acetate.

Other Latex Coatings.   There is no reason why acrylate, styrene-butadiene, vinyl, or any other type of latex can not be formulated to give heat sealable coatings for plastic films. To date, however, none of these other materials has shown sufficient advantages over those systems already in use to warrant the development of the necessary technology.

Other Lacquer Coatings. Materials such as polyvinyl acetal, polyvinyl formal, polyvinyl butyral, ethyl cellulose all can be formulated to give heat sealable coatings. These polymers generally are more expensive than vinyl chloride copolymers and so have found limited use. Vinyl chloride copolymer lacquer coatings are being used by one cellophane manufacturer and could be developed into coatings for other films or paper.

Coating Adhesion. Regardless of whether the coating is latex or lacquer, it must adhere strongly to the substrate to provide a functional heat seal coating. Otherwise, heat seal strengths will be only as strong as the adhesive bond between coating and substrate. It is generally desirable then to have heat seals fail in cohesion rather than in adhesion. Unfortunately, most coatings show little or no adhesion to the unmodified surfaces of either plastic films or cellophane. Adhesion is obtained in several different ways. Adhesion promoting agents can be included in the regenerated cellulose composition which becomes cellophane. Other plastic films are more readily surface modified by post treatment, such as corona arc discharge, flame treatment, chlorination, UV irradiation or electron bombardment. Even these treatments may not be adequate to obtain the desired level of adhesion between given coating and substrate combinations. It may still be necessary to use one of the adhesion promoting primers of the type discussed in Chapter 6.

Table 3.9 shows the effect of corona arc discharge on adhesion of an 80 : 20 vinyl chloride: acrylonitrile copolymer lacquer (20% in MEK) to oriented polypropylene film. Another facet of heat sealable coating is

TABLE 3.9.*   Effect of Corona Arc Discharge on Coating Adhesion**

Sample	Coating Thickness (mils)	Heat Seal Strength (gm/in.)
Unmodified polypropylene film	.06	280
	.12	400
Corona arc discharge treated polypropylene film	.06	460
	.12	680

* British Patent 920,078 (March 6, 1963).
** 80 : 20 vinyl chloride : acrylonitrile copolymer (20 % in MEK).

evident from this information. Heat seal strengths decrease with decreasing coating thickness, and this factor has to be taken into account in the design of a coating system.

Heat seal strengths that are obtained on coated films seldom exceed 500 gm/in. and are useful at levels as low as 100 gm/in. (see Figure 3.4 and Table 3.10). Heat seals on coated paper, where adhesion is obtained by mechanical interlocking of the coating with the paper fibers, may be in excess of 1,000 gm/in. Usually the heat seal strengths of coated films are considerably lower than those which can be obtained with thicker extrusion coatings of polyethylene.

Coating Application Methods.

Latexes   The most widely used application method utilizes the air knife metering system shown in Figures 3.5 and 3.6. Here an excess of coating is applied to the web by the color roll, which is rotating in the latex supply pan. The web then passes over the breast roll, where a

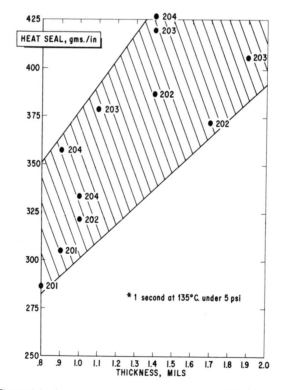

Figure 3.4.   Heat seal vs. thickness for duPont "K" cellophane.

TABLE 3.10. Heat Seal Strengths of Typical Cellophanes

Type	Temp. (°C)	Psi	Dwell Time (sec)	Seal Strength (gm/in.)
Avisco 300DS	105	42.2	1	265
Avisco 300 M-1		No seal		
Avisco 300 MS-1	105	42.2	1	44
Avisco 300 MSB-7	105	42.2	1	260
Avisco 300 MS-3	110	42.2	1	118
Avisco 300 MS-4	110	42.2	1	238
DuPont 300 MSD-52	105	42.2	1	202
DuPont 300 MSD-53	110	42.2	1	112
DuPont 300 MSD-54	105	42.2	1	195
DuPont 300 LSD	105	42.2	1	285

Slip values range from .16–.30.

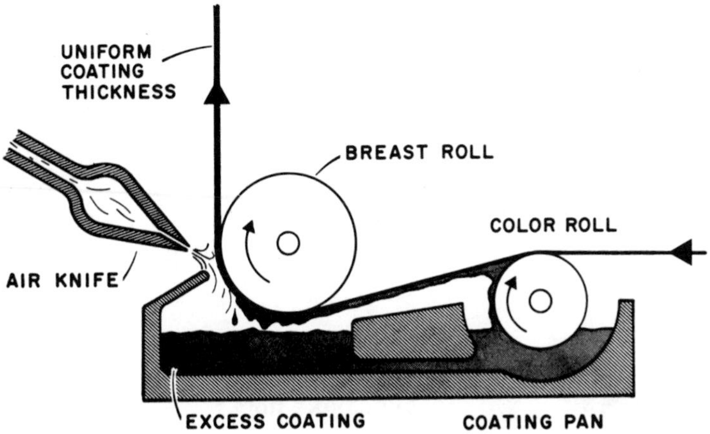
UNIFORM COATING THICKNESS
BREAST ROLL
COLOR ROLL
AIR KNIFE
EXCESS COATING
COATING PAN

Figure 3.5. Air knife detail. Air knife coating method.

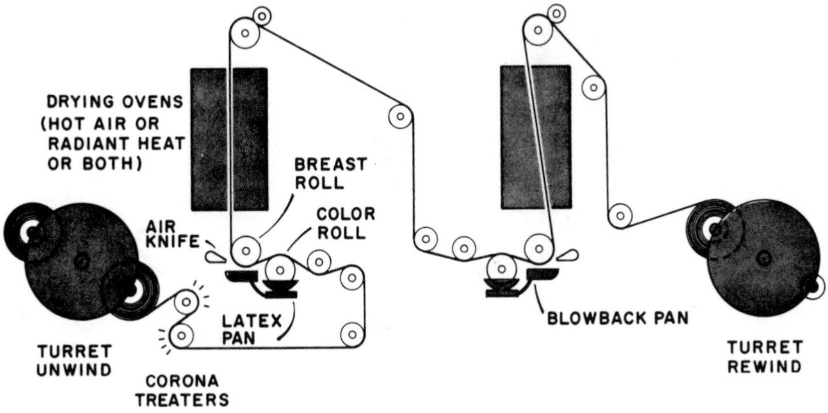
DRYING OVENS (HOT AIR OR RADIANT HEAT OR BOTH)
BREAST ROLL
AIR KNIFE
COLOR ROLL
LATEX PAN
BLOWBACK PAN
TURRET UNWIND
CORONA TREATERS
TURRET REWIND

Figure 3.6. Typical air knife coating line. Both sides of web can be coated in single pass.

precisely controlled jet of air from the air knife blows off the excess coating into a recirculating system at the same time that it smooths the coating's surface. This metering method has been used successfully to apply uniform thickness latex coatings to paper at speeds in excess of 2,000 fpm. Plastic films are seldom coated at speeds much above 500 fpm. This metering method is well-suited to plastic webs, since it does a "contour" coating job. That is, it puts the same coating thickness on the thick and thin sections of the web. This is important because the gauge variation of many plastic webs is seldom much less than $\pm$ 10%. This gauge variation may be greater than the desired coating thickness so that any coating method which applies an absolutely flat surfaced coating is going to put too little coating on the thick sections and too much on the thin sections. Coating weight is varied by changing such variables as air knife gap, distance of air knife from the web, angle of air knife, air pressure supplied to the air knife, and coating solids contents.

Lacquers   Figure 3.7 illustrates gravure printing. This is the most broadly applicable method for coating plastic webs with lacquers. The gravure roll rotates in the lacquer bath, excess coating is scraped from the surface with a doctor blade, and then a pattern of coating is transferred to the film surface at the rubber roll nip. This pattern may flow together to give a uniform coating, but usually smoothing bars are

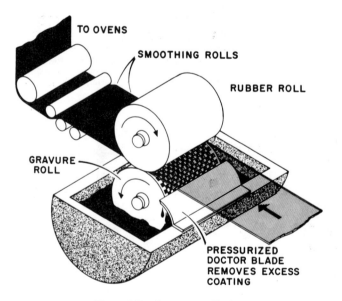

Figure 3.7.   Gravure applicator.

required to assist in the leveling. Gravure printing is also a "contour" coating process. Coating weight is varied by changing the solids content in the lacquer or by replacing the gravure roll with one having a larger or a smaller engraved surface pattern. Many more complex variations of this simple technique are used, and the reader is referred to coating machinery manufacturers for further detailed information. The use of solvent-based coatings requires explosionproof equipment as well as solvent recovery units to keep coating costs down.

Both gravure and air knife metering techniques are limited to one side coating operations. Either can be used to apply latex or lacquer, but the air knife is overall better suited to latex coating while the gravure method appears best suited to lacquer coating.

Where a highly uniform thickness substrate ($\pm$ 1–2% gauge variation) is to be coated, a simpler coating technique is available which coats both sides simultaneously. Cellophane is the only substrate, so far developed, which has the required uniform gauge profile. Figure 3.8 illustrates the technique. Here, the base film passes through a dip bath and picks up an excess of coating on both sides. This film then passes between precision finished metering rolls which are adjusted to an opening just wide enough to pass the film plus the desired amount of coating on both sides. Since this coater operates at relatively high speed

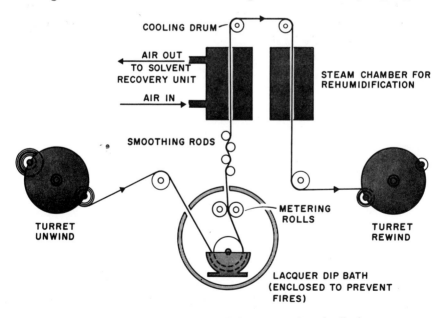

Figure 3.8.   Simultaneous two side lacquer coating of cellophane.

(400–700 fpm), the film is forced to the precise center of the metering nip opening by the hydraulic pressure exerted by the coating on both sides. Thus, a uniform coating thickness is applied to both sides. After passing the nip, the wet coating is usually smoothed by small diameter smoothing rods and then must be completely dried before it contacts the next roll. Drying towers for coated cellophane may be as high as 60 feet. During the drying the substrate becomes somewhat desiccated and must be rehumidified before being rewound. This is accomplished by passing the film through a steam chamber which may also be up to 60 feet long. The steam treatment drives water into the cellophane substrate and restores it to the desired pliable and tough state which is found in cellophane having an optimum water content. This type of coating equipment can be used with either latex or lacquer type coatings.

Summary.   The consumption of coated plastic films seems destined to increase steadily in the future as more manufacturers become skilled in this technology. The overall film properties which can be obtained by applying thin coatings to various substrates cannot be obtained as inexpensively in any other way. In particular, polyvinylidene chloride coated paper and heat seal coated oriented polypropylene have favorable growth prospects. The latter may gain much of its growth at the expense of coated cellophanes, but its invasion of the established markets will probably be slow.

FOUR

testing methods

CARL O. RASPOR

INTRODUCTION

This chapter is primarily concerned with those tests and test methods which are peculiar to thin film and sheet up to 30 mils in thickness. An attempt is made to allot space to the description and discussion of these tests commensurate with their overall importance in the field of thin film and sheeting. In assessing the significance of a given property for plastic film, one must consider not only the end use of the film, but also the processes which the film must undergo before it can be put to such use. For example, optical properties of a film are important when it is used as a bakery product overwrap material; flatness is of little consequence. Conversely, film flatness *is* important in a coating operation, but optical properties are not.

To place these tests in their proper perspective, something should be said about certain considerations which are common to all of them: variability of test results, conditioning and isotropy of test specimens, calibration of testing machines, and usefulness of tests for predicting film performance in actual service.

In the case of plastic materials in general and thin films in particular, it is not at all unusual to observe a large variation in experimental results when nominally identical samples are subjected to nominally identical test conditions. This experimental scatter is not observed with all films to the same extent nor in all tests to the same degree. Several factors, not all of which are readily apparent, can account for such deviations. Among these are batch-to-batch variations either·in the basic polymer or in the film manufacturing and postmanufacturing process; point-to-point variations on a single sample illustrated by the effects of nonuniform bubble orientation; additional differences in the test specimens such as the presence or absence of minute notches or other stress concentrators; and even undetected differences in the testing procedure itself. The latter item is exemplified by a case where two identical samples of a given material are not clamped in *exactly* the same way in the jaws of a tensile tester, thereby setting up different stress distributions in the two test specimens.

The dependence of physical properties of plastics on test environment is a well-established fact. Temperature in particular, must be adequately regulated but control of humidity and electromagnetic radiation may be equally critical factors for some films. For this reason it is necessary that test samples should all be subjected to the same environmental conditions after manufacture in order that test variations be reduced to a minimum. Of course, if it has been independently established that the type of film in question is unaffected by exposure to certain environments, the precautions to be taken can be reduced accordingly. In this connection it should be noted that the properties of a film may change during the test itself and no amount of care or conditioning can eliminate this undesirable element. For example, at the start of a certain gas permeability test, one side of a plasticized film specimen is exposed to approximately vacuum conditions and the ether side to a nonzero pressure of the gas whose permeability rate is desired. Under these conditions the plasticizer volatilizes to some extent into the vacuum during the test, thereby indicating a false test-gas transmission rate, and, furthermore, leaving the residual film with different barrier characteristics than it had with all plasticizer present.

On the other hand, a fetish need not be made of *exact* repetitive test conditions. For many materials and for many purposes it makes little practical difference if a tensile test is carried out at 23°C or 28°C. Common sense is the rule here as elsewhere and the test conditions should not be made any more stringent than necessary to obtain the type of data required.

Many oriented films are anisotropic. Their properties vary with the direction in which they are measured in the plane of the film. Until the isotropy of a film is established, it is advisable to test a given sample in two mutually perpendicular planar directions. The usual choices are the machine direction (that in which the film travels during manufacture) and the transverse direction (perpendicular to the machine direction in the plane of the film). The directional dependence of tear, tensile, elongation and other properties is usually readily apparent when the sample is tested in the machine and transverse directions.

The subject of machine calibration is interjected solely to call attention to this aspect of testing. Too often a machine is used for test purposes time after time under the assumption that it is operating properly. An American Society for Testing and Materials (ASTM) Standard E4-64[1] deals with this matter as far as loadmeasuring machines are concerned. Nothing further will be said about the problem here because it is not peculiar to film testing.

Lastly, a few general remarks about the practical usefulness of these tests follow. Many of these procedures are not accepted industry-wide standards, but were developed by various groups to solve particular, often very specific, problems. Therefore, when considering the use of a test already in existence, some thought should be given to the purpose of the testing. Unless this is done, needless time, effort, and money may be expended. As an illustration of this point, if one contemplates using a water vapor transmission test to predict the shelf life of a product that is sensitive to moisture, one would naturally select the test and conditions that duplicate as nearly as possible the actual use situation. Since it is highly unlikely that the conditions under which a test is run will *exactly* duplicate shelf conditions, this fact should be recognized beforehand as an inherent limitation on the valid use of test results for predictive purposes. Moreover, testing that is used as part of a research program on production or customer problems often requires a different approach than testing used for establishing specifications and maintaining quality control.

The film testing methods will now be treated, but only in terms of general principles and procedures. This restriction is made because the principal aim of this chapter is not to provide a manual of testing methods, but rather to present a broad view of test methods that are currently available and some idea of why one is used in preference to another. Detailed information on any test is provided in the references. The various methods used to measure a given property will be introduced according to the following scheme. First, the ASTM method will be outlined (if there is one) and its significant features pointed out. Then tests which differ only slightly from the ASTM test will be considered with some brief statements regarding the advantages and disadvantages of the changes. Finally, other tests which are fairly well known will be described.

At the close of this chapter appear three sections whose topics are only marginally related to physical property testing: identification of films, thickness measurements, and yield.

GAS PERMEABILITY

The current ASTM Standard on this subject,[2] D1434-66, distinguishes between the two quantities, Gas Transmission Rate and Permeability Coefficient.

The Gas Transmission Rate (GTR) is defined as the volume of gas that passes through a sample of unit area under unit pressure differential, the rate being determined after the slope of the transmitted volume–time curve has become constant. The temperature and specimen thickness must also be given as an integral part of the GTR.

The Permeability Coefficient represents a more fundamental property and is independent of the geometry of the test sample since it is defined in terms of unit thickness. It is the product of the solubility of the gas in the film and the diffusion rate of the gas through the film.

GTR's are usually expressed in cc (at 0°C and 76 cm Hg) per sq m 24 hr atm, cc per 100 sq in. 24 hr atm or cu in. per 100 sq in. 24 hr atm. Rates expressed in one set of units may be converted to other systems with the aid of Table 4.1.

TABLE 4.1.   Permeability Conversion Factors

to go from	to	multiply by
cc per sq m 24 hr atm	cc per 100 sq in. 24 hr atm	.0645
cc per sq m 24 hr atm	cu in. per 100 sq in. 24 hr atm	.00394
cc per 100 sq in. 24 hr atm	cu in. per 100 sq in. 24 hr atm	.061

Although not generally recommended by ASTM, GTR's are sometimes referred to on a "per mil" basis regardless of the thickness of film that was tested. This is accomplished by multiplying the measured GTR of the film by its thickness in mils, the assumption being made that the GTR is inversely proportional to film thickness.

GTR values per mil (in cc per 100 sq in. 24 hr atm) for oxygen through plastic films range from below 1.0 for certain types of saran to 300 for medium density polyethylene and even much higher for other polymers.

ASTM provides two methods for measuring GTR. Figure 4.1 is a schematic diagram of the apparatus used in Method M (Manometric). With the test specimen in place and all of the mercury in the reservoir, the cell system below the specimen is evacuated. This is followed by evacuation of the test gas chamber (not shown, but mounted immediately above the test specimen). Mercury is then poured into the reservoir and capillary arms. Test gas is admitted to the upper chamber until the desired driving pressure is attained. In most cases this pressure is one atmosphere. As the gas passes through the film, the pressure below the film sample increases. This pressure change, as measured by depression of the mercury column, is converted to a volume using the ideal gas law. For obvious reasons this method is classed as a pressure-increase method.

ASTM method V (Volumetric) uses a different test apparatus. The film specimen separates two compartments as before, but in this case the lower pressure chamber is maintained at a pressure of approximately one atmosphere instead of near zero. The GTR is obtained by observing

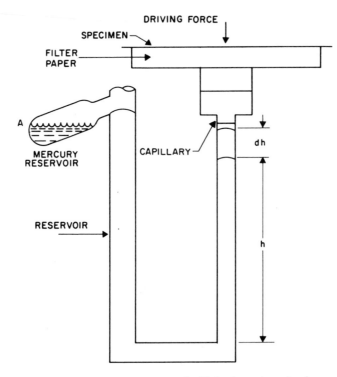

Figure 4.1.   Gas transmission cell with test specimen in place.

directly the volume of test gas passing through the film as a function of time. Method V is very similar to another procedure[3] described below.

A modification to the ASTM test apparatus (Method M) has been made[4] which permits easier insertion and removal of the test specimen and also allows the test area of the film sample to be changed.

A portable apparatus has been designed [3] which requires no mercury, vacuum system or electrical connections. The test gas from a small cylinder A (Figure 4.2) passes through a pressure regulator B into a chamber C mounted immediately above the film D. The transmitted gas displaces a slug of water E (injected through needle F) inside the capillary tubing. The permeation rate is determined by measuring the time required for the slug to move a given distance along the calibrated tubing. The results obtained using this apparatus compare favorably with those obtained using the ASTM apparatus and procedure (Method M). This portable unit is not easily used with highly impermeable film or sheet or, obviously, with moisture sensitive films.

Another device is also used for measuring gas permeabilities.[5] It consists of two chambers separated by the test piece. The downstream side is continuously evacuated and the change in volume of test gas as a function of time at constant pressure is recorded.

A possible disadvantage of ASTM Method M was alluded to earlier. One side of the test specimen is exposed to a vacuum and if the film contains essential materials which are volatile (plasticizers or moisture, for example) these materials may volatilize, thereby changing the film permeability characteristics. One way to avoid this situation[6] is to use two different gases, both at one atmosphere pressure, one on each side

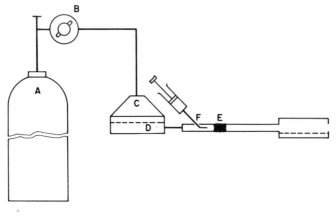

Figure 4.2. Portable test cell.

of the film. In these circumstances, each gas exerts a partial pressure of one atmosphere on one side of the film and zero partial pressure on the other side. The difference in *partial* pressures causes the gas to transmit through the test specimen. A gas chromatograph or other means is then used to analyze the gas mixture on the side of the film opposite to that of the test gas. Transmission values obtained by this method agree with those obtained by using more conventional procedures. It is possible with this technique to determine *simultaneously* the GTR's of two gases. To do this, the gas mixture is analyzed on each side of the film sample.

A further advantage of this particular apparatus is the large (8-inch diameter) test sample used compared to the usual 3-inch diameter test piece. This test belongs to the class of concentration-increase methods.

A comparison was made among three different permeability tests each based on a different principle: concentration-increase, pressure-increase and volume-increase.[7] The results obtained by these three methods correlate quite well but not perfectly. No one method has outstanding advantages over the others, but each has certain features which are desirable depending on the circumstances.

A recent paper[8] presents a method which appears to be the most flexible one of all, although the associated equipment is quite expensive. The film specimen separates two compartments which are initially evacuated. Test gas is introduced into one of the chambers and a mass spectrometer is used to detect and "count" the molecules of permeating gas. The technique has several attractive features. By this method one can measure (1) the amount and kind of any additives that are given off by the film into the low pressure chamber during the test, (2) permeability rates of several gases at one time, and (3) permeability of gases in the presence of vapors. Furthermore, the apparatus is very sensitive so that rates as low as .01 cc (STP) per 100 sq in. 24 hr atm can be measured. Results from this method compare favorably with those obtained using ASTM Method M.

WATER VAPOR PERMEABILITY

The relevant ASTM Standard is E96-66.[9] The test film is fastened over the mouth of a cup containing either a desiccant or water. This sealed cup is then placed in a controlled atmosphere of specified temperature and humidity. From the weight gain or loss of this unit a rate of water vapor transmission through the film can be calculated. The water vapor transmission rate, WVTR or MVTR, is the flow rate of water vapor through a unit area of film after the steady state has been reached. It is often expressed in units of gm/24 hr sq m or gm/24 hr 100 sq in. To convert from a rate expressed in terms of sq m to the same rate expressed in terms of 100 sq in., multiply by .0645. Values of WVTR range from less than .1 gm/24 hr 100 sq in. (95°F and 90% relative humidity) for certain grades of saran through .5 for low density polyethylene to 30 or more for ethyl cellulose.

Again, as in the case of gas permeabilities, the WVTR is sometimes converted to a "per mil" basis, but this is not always a valid transformation.

Water Vapor Permeance, defined as the ratio WVTR/vapor pressure difference across the film, and Water Vapor Permeability, equal to the Permeance multiplied by film thickness, are alternative ways of expressing water vapor transmission rate, but they are not often used in the literature.

A rather simple procedure, similar in principle to the ASTM method, consists of putting desiccant in a bag made of the film to be tested[10] and measuring the weight gain with time. Results from this test were compared to those obtained from a version of the ASTM method and found to agree within experimental error, generally.

In another type of water vapor transmission test[11] the membrane to be tested separates two chambers, both of which are initially evacuated. Water vapor is introduced into one of the chambers at a certain vapor pressure. The vapor pressure in the other chamber due to water diffusion through the film is measured as a function of time. From these data and the geometry of the system a WVTR can be calculated.

The hygrophotographic technique[12] uses a special photographic plate which is sensitive to moisture as well as light. The plate is put in a sealed bag made of the film to be tested, and color changes of the plate caused by permeated water vapor are used as a basis for determining a WVTR.

An electronic WVT tester has been devised[13,14] which is claimed to yield more reproducible results than the ASTM method. Also, this method requires only minutes to determine a rate, whereas standard techniques require hours or even days. The test specimen separates two compartments. Initially, one contains water and the other is at a low relative humidity (R.H.). When the water vapor passes through the film into the low R.H. chamber, it is detected by a sensor whose electrical resistance is very sensitive to R.H. The rate of change of R.H. in the "dry" chamber is used to calculate the WVTR.

A journal article[15] discusses water vapor permeability through multiple barriers and points out how the various aspects of end use will determine in which order the barriers should be stacked for best results. The authors conclude that (1) doubling the number of layers of a given polymeric film will double the barrier effects and (2) for a combined film in which one component has a pressure-dependent permeability coefficient, the most impermeable film should face the high humidity environment. As far as testing is concerned, these results emphasize the importance of properly disposing the film specimen(s) during a permeability test so that experimental results have the desired predictive value.

FLAMMABILITY

A burning rate can be determined by following the procedure given in ASTM Standard D568-61.[16] The end of a standard-size strip of film is ignited and the time required to burn a certain length of this strip is recorded. Provision is made for classifying nonburning and self-extinguishing films. Another flammability test, different in its mechanics but fundamentally quite similar, is provided in ASTM Standard D1433–58.[17] In both tests film shrinkage may invalidate the results.

SOLVENT RESISTANCE

This is a crucial property for film applications involving ink and adhesive formulations, lacquer coatings, and extraction of plasticizers or other additives. Determination of the resistance of films to chemical reagents is the subject of ASTM Standard D543-67.[18] This test consists of immersing the specimen in a standard reagent for a given length of time and determining the dimensional and/or physical property changes which result from the action of the solvent on the film.

Resistance to extraction by chemicals is covered by ASTM Standard D1239-55.[19] The procedure to be followed is essentially the same as that of D543-67, but only the weight loss due to immersion in a solvent is measured since this is the major physical property change as far as extraction is concerned.

BURSTING STRENGTH

Bursting strength may be measured by a method described in ASTM Standard D774-67.[20] This test has been widely used both in the paper industry and in the plastics field for many years. The sample to be tested is gripped between two annular clamps and over a flexible diaphragm. Hydraulic pressure expands this diaphragm against the film and causes it to bulge. The pressure is increased until the film ruptures and the pressure at rupture is called the bursting strength. This quantity gives a rough indication of film toughness but does not appear to correlate very well with any other strength measurement.

Developments in this area include a more versatile apparatus which uses air pressure as the force mechanism and which permits strain measurements to be made on the film as it is extended.[21]

The strength of plastic bags can be evaluated by means of a simple bursting device.[22] The bag is subjected to air pressure at a controlled rate of increase and the pressure of failure is noted.

FOLDING ENDURANCE

A folding test based on the MIT paper tester is described in ASTM Tentative D2176–63T.[23] One end of the test piece is clamped in a stationary jaw while the other is in an oscillating grip. Tension is applied through the fixed jaw. The overall effect of this unit is to cause four folds to be made in the film for each complete cycle of oscillation (see Figure 4.3). The number of flexes before failure are counted and this figure is used as a measure of the folding endurance of the sample.

A low temperature flexing test has also been devised.[24] In this test the specimen is subjected to an oscillating force applied to the ends of the strip, thereby alternately buckling and extending the film.

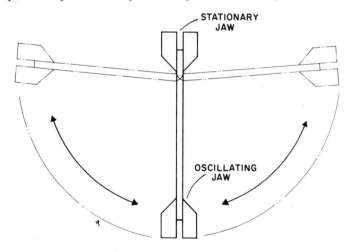

Figure 4.3.   M.I.T. folding endurance tester.

IMPACT RESISTANCE

This property is a measure of the ability of a material to absorb energy in a very short period of time and usually is regarded as that measured property most closely related to the somewhat vague quality called toughness. Impact resistance is also related to brittleness. Brittleness denotes the lack of ductility, poor flexing properties, or more generally, a lack of toughness. It is highly dependent on the rate at which the stress is applied. For this reason brittleness tests are included in this section.

The field of impact testing is characterized by a large number of tests often not measuring the same fundamental quantity. Furthermore, the tests are not always well understood theoretically. The tests, for example, are made on specimens of different sizes, under varying complicated stress distributions and at different rates of loading. This section is mainly concerned with examples of three types of impact tests: the falling-weight test, the bag-drop test, and tensile impact tests.

The dart-drop test, ASTM Standard D1709-67,[25] is a standard test for polyethylene film but is used with other materials as well. The apparatus is sketched in Figure 4.4. With this test one determines that dart weight which will result in the fracture of 50% of the samples tested. The general procedure is as follows. A dart weight is selected which will fracture at least one of a group of ten specimens. The actual number of failures in ten trials is recorded. The dart weight is then

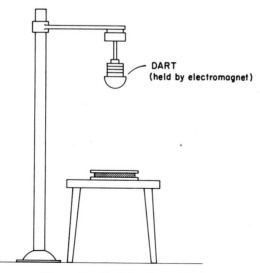

Figure 4.4.   Dart drop impact test.

changed by uniform increments and ten samples are tested at each of several dart weights with the number of failures at each weight being recorded. The data are plotted on probability graph paper, the dart weights on the linear scale and the percent failures on the probability scale. A straight line is drawn through the plotted points. The intersection of this line with the 50% probability line is the impact failure weight or impact resistance expressed in grams.

Another impact test[26] consists of projecting a small steel ball by pressurizing air through the film. The residual energy of the ball is determined after rupture of the specimen and an impact strength is calculated from the energy lost in causing the failure.

In the bag-drop test,[27] a sealed bag made of the material to be tested and containing a specified weight of sand (or other suitable material) is dropped from rest and falls onto a rigid surface. If rupture occurs, the bag is examined to see if the failure was in the seal or in the film. The test conditions should be established from a consideration of the end use of the film. The results may be expressed in several ways. Two that have been suggested are to state how many drops could be made from a given height without failure or the percentage of failures which occur when a series of identical bags are dropped from a given height. It is obvious that a theoretical analysis of this test would be difficult, if not impossible, but even so the test may have practical value. This test may require considerable time unless the bags are machine-made.

A study of the role of rate of deformation in film brittleness in a bag-drop test was made.[28] The rate in this test was found to be of the order of 100,000–200,000%/minute.

A probe burst test is also described in the latter reference. It is somewhat like the dart-drop test, but here the dart, instead of falling freely, is attached to the crosshead of a tensile tester. The mechanism is so arranged that as the crosshead (attached to a strain gauge) falls at a constant rate, the rigidly mounted dart penetrates the film, which is held in an annular clamp. The stress-strain curve for this deformation is recorded, just as in an ordinary tensile test.

Current interest appears to be centered in the area of tensile impact testing. One of the reasons for this interest is the comparatively simple geometry of the test, and so it lends itself to some theoretical interpretations. The test is simple in principle and can be visualized as an ordinary tensile test wherein the specimen is loaded at a rate of thousands of inches per minute instead of the usual 20 inches per minute or less. There are many different ways in which impact loading is achieved. These loading methods make use of a freely falling weight, a falling pendulum, or a rotating flywheel, for example.[29,32] It should be noted that tensile impact tests usually require relatively complex equipment and are therefore not well suited for routine testing.

It has been pointed out[33] that a single numerical value for impact strength is insufficient to characterize the behavior of a film under an impact loading. The *way* in which energy is absorbed by the specimen as a function of time is important, too. This experimental fact is the rationale for the design of a pendulum-type tensile impact tester, which measures *both* the energy lost by the pendulum in rupturing the film and the load–time curve during rupture.[34]

Since it has been observed that plastic bags often fail as a result of *repeated* impacts, an impact fatigue test was developed.[35] The main features of the test are provision for identical repeated impacts and for a uniform time interval between impacts.

A simple test for film brittleness is the hand-flex test. The film is grasped in both hands and flexed rapidly for a few seconds and then examined for cracks and pinholes. The test is very crude but it may be helpful in rating films which differ widely in brittleness.

A mechanized version of the hand-flex test is also used.[36] Both the manual and machine flex tests measure an aspect of toughness relating to rupture resistance when sharp corners and folds are present in the film.

Judging by literature references, the ASTM test for film brittleness as a function of temperature, D1790-62,[37] is little used. In this test a bent loop of film is subjected to a compressive impact force.

MAR RESISTANCE

Following ASTM Standard D1044-56,[38] the surface of a specimen is subjected to an abrasive action and then the light scattering properties of the abraded area are determined and compared to those of the original unmarred sample.

In ASTM Standard D673-44,[39] the film surface is abraded by dropping abrasive particles onto the film from a fixed height. The gloss of the marred area is measured and compared to the unabraded film to determine the mar resistance.

A third ASTM Standard, D1242-56,[40] describes a procedure wherein the surface is abraded in a standard way and the volume of material lost by the specimen due to this abrasive action is determined. The loss in volume is taken as a measure of the abrasion resistance.

STIFFNESS

The tensile modulus is often used as a measure of film stiffness. This quantity is obtained by calculating the ratio of a stress to strain at a certain point on a tensile stress–strain curve. The point at which the ratio is taken should be on the initial (linear) portion of the graph. The results of this test do not always correlate with use experience. This lack of correlation may be due in part to the fact that an accurate modulus is not easy to determine. For this reason, other stiffness tests have been developed.

In particular, a device which measures the "hand" (handle, feel) of paper or fabric was introduced and applied to the measurement of film stiffness.[41,42] This test can be understood by reference to Figure 4.5. The specimen A is placed over a slot B as shown in the figure. An end of pivoted bar C is lowered through the slot against the resistance of the film. A strain gauge detects this resistance, which is displayed in units of force. This is a very rapid test requiring only seconds.

The contention is made[42] that this stiffness tester does not distinguish between inherent film stiffness and thickness effects. Instead, it gives a measure of the combined effects, which is not necessarily a drawback. This article describes a procedure for measuring inherent stiffness only by means of a dynamic tensile modulus apparatus. One end of a narrow strip of film A is inserted into the clamp B which, in turn, is attached to the needle holder of a phonograph recording head C (see Figure 4.6). A clamp from which appropriate weights D may be hung is attached to the other end of the film. The specimen is treated as if it were a simple spring and a periodic longitudinal vibration is applied to this "spring" through the recording head. The vibration frequency is varied until the system resonates. When the resonant frequency is known, the modulus can be calculated.

Related to the preceding tests is a softness test.[43] Figure 4.7 shows a schematic diagram of the essentials of this test. A strip of film is bent

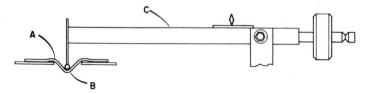

Figure 4.5.   Stiffness tester.

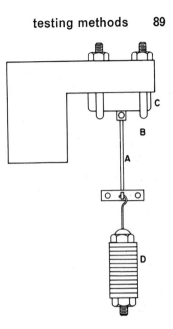

Figure 4.6.   Dynamic tensile strength apparatus.

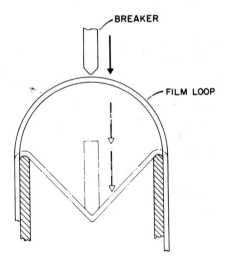

Figure 4.7.   Film softness tester.

into a loop, and a "breaker" which is attached to a strain gauge is
forced down into the vertex of the loop as shown by the dotted lines.
The force needed to distort the loop is recorded. Results of this test
correlated roughly with those of a panel of human testers who evaluated
the softness of films by their "feel."

TEAR RESISTANCE

Standard tests are available to measure two aspects of tearing, both of which may be important in the end use of films. These are tear initiation and tear propagation.

ASTM Standard D1004-66[44] details a procedure for measuring the force required to *initiate* tearing. The die-cut specimen shown in Figure 4.8 is placed in the grips of a tensile tester of the constant-rate-of-jaw-separation type and the grips are then separated at a rate of two inches per minute. The geometry of the test piece is such that a stress concentration is produced in the region of the right angle and the tear initiates at this point. The maximum stress during the tearing process is recorded as the tear initiation strength.

It is clear that the stress concentration is a critical aspect of this test. To ensure better reproducibility of the stress distribution and so of the test results, it is necessary that the specimen be free of nicks and random notches and that it be aligned properly in the tester jaws.

This test has been criticized[45] for the small distance torn, which allows local imperfections to influence the test results disproportionately for the slow tearing rate, and consequently, the effect of film extensibility on tearing; and for the difficulty in maintaining the critical 90° angle. In addition, the rate of tearing is much lower than that to which the film may be exposed in actual use.

Since no simple relationship exists between tear strength and thickness, it is generally not advisable to convert experimental results to some standard thickness.

ASTM Standard D1922-67[46] is a tear propagation test (Elmendorf). This procedure is used to measure the force required to propagate a tear through a fixed distance of film after the tear has already been started. The measurement is carried out by mounting the pre-cut test specimen (Figure 4.9) between two jaws. One jaw is fixed and the other attached to a pendulum, commonly a sector of a wheel or circle, which is held by a stop in an up position. When the pendulum is released, it swings down

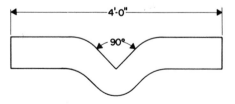

Figure 4.8.   Tear test specimen.

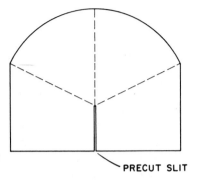

Figure 4.9.   Tear specimen for elmendorf tear
resistance test.

PRECUT SLIT

under the force of gravity and the specimen is torn from the already
begun slit. Because of the energy required to tear the film, the pendulum
has less energy than it would have had if it had fallen freely. This difference in energy is indicated by a pointer on a calibrated scale. The tearing
rate in this test is of the order of hundreds of inches per minute and
thus it approximates those encountered in many film applications.

A second tear propagation test is given in ASTM Standard D1938-
67.[47] In this test the specimen shown in Figure 4.10 is placed in the
grips of a tensile tester, tongue A in one jaw and tongue B in the other.
The grips are separated at a rate of 10 inches per minute and the stress
is recorded as in the usual tensile experiment. The stress-time curves
obtained are analyzed in different ways depending on their shape, and a
tear strength is defined. This test may be difficult to apply to films with
very low resistance to tear propagation. If this is the case, the results
may not correlate very well with actual performance, but even so they

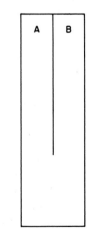

Figure 4.10.   Tensile tear specimen.

may be valuable for ranking films of similar thickness and elongation properties.

Another apparatus used to measure different aspects of tearing, the puncture propagation tear tester, is described in ASTM Standard D2582-67.[48] This apparatus measures the ability of a film to resist puncture and the propagation of that puncture. Similar to this test is another[49] which measures the tendency of a film to snag and the energy to tear the film after it has snagged. To measure this effect, both methods use a needle which strikes a film at some angle.

It is noteworthy that tear resistance is one of those properties most sensitive to orientation. To illustrate, one type of (unoriented) polypropylene film (1 mil) has a tear propagation strength of 45 gm in the machine direction and 600 gm in the transverse direction, while biaxially oriented polypropylene film has a strength of approximately 10 gm in each direction.

TENSILE PROPERTIES

This section will be confined strictly to the conventional low-rate-of-strain tensile testing methods. Tensile *impact* testing has already been discussed in the section dealing with impact resistance.

Tensile tests are usually distinguished by the manner in which the load is applied to the test specimen. Two methods of applying the load have been widely used.

In the constant-rate-of-increase-of-load method, ASTM Standard D1923-67,[50] the sample is clamped at one end by a fixed jaw and at the other by a clamp attached to a weight which is mounted on rollers capable of moving along a set of tracks, the whole assembly being mounted on a horizontal plane. The test consists of tilting the plane at a constant rate, thereby applying the load to the film sample at a constant rate of increase. The rate of grip separation varies depending on the viscoelastic properties of the test sample. This test is also known as the inclined-plane test.

Current literature indicates that the inclined-plane method is not much used today. It has largely been superseded by the constant-rate-of-grip-separation method, ASTM Standard D882-67.[51] In this test the grips holding the ends of a rectangular specimen are separated at a constant rate in the range of $\frac{1}{2}$–20 inches per minute, and an associated system records the load on the sample as a function of the grip separation until the sample breaks. An alternative to this method is to place two gauge marks on the specimen between the jaws and to measure the separation of these marks instead of the jaw separation. This latter procedure eliminates errors in determining elongation-at-break. These errors are introduced by film slippage in the grips. Some caution may be required in placing gauge marks since certain inks may act on the film to weaken it.

Although tensile breaking strengths are usually calculated on the original specimen dimensions, for films with extremely high elongations this procedure may lead to spuriously low values and it may be necessary to base calculations on the cross-sectional area at the time of break in order to arrive at a realistic figure. It is interesting to note that an apparatus has been designed[52] for use with soft films in which the load is reduced in proportion to the decrease in cross-sectional area of the test piece.

A tensile modulus (see Stiffness) may also be determined by the same apparatus that is used for measuring tensile strengths. Although modulus and tensile strength can, in principle, be found simultaneously, it is often desirable to separate these determinations to permit the use of optimum machine conditions for each property. For modulus experiments, the sample should be clamped tautly in the grips and a lower load range and higher chart speed used than for tensile strength measurement. These changes are useful in obtaining more accurate data. The modulus test may be discontinued when the load–grip separation curve deviates from linearity and the modulus is calculated as the slope of this straight line.

As has been implied above, the constant-rate-of-grip separation test is not always a constant-rate-of-strain test due to slippage in the grips. In practice this is not usually significant, but for some materials in which rate-of-strain has a strong influence on the measured property, use of a true-rate-of-strain test would be advisable, even though such methods are more complicated.

The cutting of film tensile specimens is dealt with in an article published in an ASTM journal.[53] Results show that die-cutting should not be used because it notches the specimen. Furthermore, a manually-operated razor blade or shear-cutting are the best methods now available.

When attempting to relate the results of a *uniaxial* tensile test, such as have been discussed above, to actual performance, it should be recognized that in use a film will generally be subjected to biaxial tension. It has been shown[54] that the difference in behavior of a material when subjected to uniaxial and biaxial stressing may be considerable.

To measure the strength of a heat seal,[55] the free ends of a standard-size sealed film specimen are gripped by the jaws of a tensile tester as shown in Figure 4.11 and the movable jaw is driven downward at a constant rate, peeling the sealed area apart. The strength of the seal is defined as the maximum force indicated in the test per inch of seal width.

Sealed films which do not peel smoothly and are of high strength may present a testing problem. For seals of this type a fusion temperature can be defined. It is that sealing temperature which results in a seal which cannot be separated even by slow and careful hand delamination. This temperature can be found by making seals (at constant time and pressure) at various temperatures until that temperature is reached at which a fusion seal results.

OPTICAL PROPERTIES

It has become customary to distinguish three properties of films which are generally categorized as "opticals": gloss, haze, and transparency. These are of most significance for polyolefins where changes in

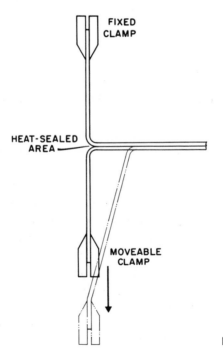

Figure 4.11. Heat seal testing.

film processing conditions can have marked effects on the optical properties of the film.

Gloss refers to the shiny appearance of a plastic film and is defined in terms of the ability of a surface to reflect light regularly. ASTM Tentative D2457-65T[56] gives one test designed to measure specular gloss. A parallel beam of light is shone onto the film surface at an angle of incidence of 60° (or some other angle, if more appropriate) and a receptor is placed in such a position that it measures the light flux reflected in the mirror (specular) direction; that is, reflected at an angle of reflection of 60°. The fraction of incident light flux that is reflected in the mirror direction is the specular gloss. The 45° gloss for biaxially oriented polypropylene film is above 95 whereas the gloss of some commercial polyethylenes is about 80.

The deficiencies of certain gloss tests have been emphasized and a new test suggested.[57] The shortcomings cited are associated with the fact that the relationship between specular reflection (gloss) and angle of incidence (angle of illumination) is not the same for all films. Therefore, any test which specifies only one or a few angles of illumination has an inherent weakness which limits its usefulness. The improved test is carried out by measuring the specularly reflected light (gloss) as a function of illuminating angle, plotting the gloss vs. illuminating angle from 0° to 90° and calculating the area under this curve. An "effective gloss" is then defined as the ratio of the area so obtained to the area obtained when light incident over the same range of angles is reflected from an ideal specimen such as a mirror.

Haze is the property often referred to as cloudiness and is quantified by measuring the percent of transmitted light which, in passing through a film, is deviated greater than a certain angle from the beam direction by forward scattering. A current standard test for measuring haze is given in ASTM Standard D1003-61.[58] The hazemeter has a highly reflecting interior surface with a photoelectric cell mounted at 90° to a narrow beam of light passing through a pair of holes in the sphere (Figure 4.12). The sphere is rotatable so that the light trap may be in or out of line with the beam. With the light on, no specimen in position and the light trap out of line with the beam, the galvanometer connected to the photocell gives a reading which indicates the intensity of the total incident light, T_1. With the film specimen in place and the other conditions unchanged, the quantity measured is the total light transmitted by the sample, T_2. The specimen is now removed and the sphere is rotated so that the light trap absorbs most of the beam.

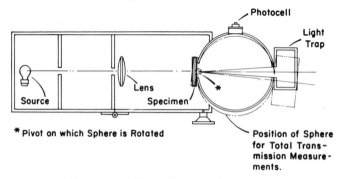

Figure 4.12.   Pivotable-sphere hazemeter.

The galvanometer measures the light scattered by the instrument, T_3. The specimen is put back in position and the light scattered by both instrument and film is measured and designated as T_4. Haze (%) is defined as $T_d/T_t \times 100$, where

$$T_t = T_2/T_1 \qquad \text{and} \qquad T_d = \frac{T_4 - T_3(T_2/T_1)}{T_1}.$$

Because of the configuration of the apparatus, only that light which is scattered more than about 2.5° from the incident beam is actually measured in T_3 and T_4.

One objection to this test[59] is that it does not measure the scattering as a function of angle and so two films with the same value for haze, as computed by the procedures of ASTM D1003-61, may actually *appear* differently when observed visually. Typically values of haze are 1–2% for biaxially oriented polypropylene film and 5–6% for polyethylene, although haze can be much larger than this for some types of polyolefin films.

It appears that gloss is related in an inverse manner to haze, but the exact relationship has not as yet been established.[59,60]

A clarity meter was designed[61] to more closely approximate a real packaging situation wherein light by which the packaged object is viewed passes through the film *twice*. Figure 4.13 shows the essentials of this apparatus. The mirror corresponds to the packaged object. The ratio of photocell readings with and without film in the path of the beam is interpreted as a measure of film clarity. The results of this test correlate with those obtained by the usual haze test (ASTM D1003-61) and with a visual test in which cards are wrapped in the test film, but they do not correlate with the results of the "see-through" test (see below).

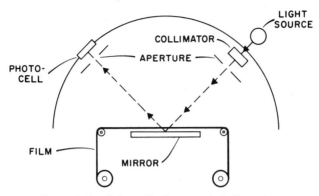

Figure 4.13.   Schematic diagram of clarity meter.

Transparency or "see through" refers to the capability of seeing objects through a film without loss of detail caused by blurring or distortion. A film of low transparency may be almost haze free. When the intensity of light transmitted through a film is plotted as a function of scattering angle, it is found that *narrow* angle scatter correlates with transparency as determined visually.[62] ASTM Tentative D1746-62T[63] is based on this known relationship between specular transmittance and "see through." This test measures the light transmitted by a film within a cone of semi-angle of three minutes about the normal to the specimen. The ratio of light flux transmitted by the film to the incident light is equal to the specular transmittance divided by 100. A more recent article claims[64] that transparency depends on both large- and small-angle scattering and describes an apparatus for measuring scattering within a very small angle.

The question of film clarity is treated at some length in a British article[65] and a visual test is described as well as a narrow-angle scattering test. The scattering test is similar in principle to the ASTM method of the preceding paragraph. The visual test consists of observing the maximum distance behind a film at which standard-size letters (for an optometrist's chart, for example) can be distinguished when viewed through the film being tested. The film is kept at a fixed distance from the eye (14 inches) and standard lighting is used. It is found that observers may rank films in the same order by means of this procedure, while "see-through distance" itself is not a very reproducible quantity.

BLOCKING

Blocking is the adhesion between two layers of film in contact which occurs under moderate pressures during processing, use, or storage.

Two aspects of blocking have been isolated: the degree of blocking and susceptibility to blocking.

ASTM Standard D1893-67[66] is concerned with measuring the *degree* of blocking. The principle of this method can be understood by reference to Figure 4.14. The metal frame is clamped in the movable jaw of a constant-rate-of-grip-separation tensile tester. The specimen (two blocked layers) to be tested is clamped in the fixed jaw as shown. The test consists of moving the lower jaw downward at a rate of five inches per minute. As the jaw moves it draws the frame and rod downward. The motion of the rod causes the layers of film to separate, and the force required to perform the separation is recorded on a chart in the usual manner. This process continues until the layers are completely separated. The blocking force is taken as the average force measured during the test.

The degree of blocking prevailing in rolls of film can be specified by measuring the force per unit width of film needed to unwind film from the roll.[67]

A qualitative way of expressing blocking is to hand test the amount of adhesion between two sheets and to classify according to the following scheme:[68]

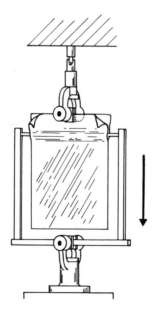

Figure 4.14.   Blocking test.

No blocking: No adhesion between the films. No resistance to sliding.

Very slight blocking: The films do not slide freely but will do so when a small force is applied.

Slight blocking: The films do not slide relative to each other but can be peeled apart. Film surfaces are intact after peeling.

Blocking: The films cannot be peeled apart without damage to their surfaces.

Another widely used blocking test measures tendency to block. Two layers of film are placed in contact under a slight pressure (1 psi) at a fixed elevated temperature for 24 hours. After this period of time the degree of blocking is measured. Test results correlate in a general way with storage experience of film in roll form. The test is useful in describing the behavior of coated films which often have blocking tendencies due to solvent retention. In fact, testing for susceptibility to blocking is often used as a means of detecting solvent retention in coated films and laminates.

ELECTROSTATIC PROPERTIES

Some simple qualitative methods for measuring the static accumulation on plastic materials have been described in the literature.[69] In one common test the sample to be tested is lowered over a pile of cigarette ashes. The distance between specimen and ashes at which ashes are attracted to the specimen is taken as a measure of the charge on the plastic. In a second test the film is supported vertically and carbon black dust is blown onto it. The dusted film is tapped to remove excess dust and it is then visually examined. If any charges are present, they show up as areas which retain dust.

Surface resistivity is also used as a measure of antistatic properties but the tests are difficult to make and to relate to acceptable antistatic performance.

A qualitative test for measuring static properties is proposed[70] to avoid certain difficulties. This device, a "static propensity tester," measures the rates of build-up and decay of an electric potential applied to a film specimen. Using these rates as a basis, a test procedure is suggested which can be used to characterize the antistatic behavior of polymers. This method has been adapted for measuring the electrostatic characteristics of polyethylene film.[71]

It is claimed[72] that static measuring devices based on charge generation by friction are not a reliable means for measuring electrostatic properties since during generation of a charge, it is difficult to keep the rubbing areas constant and to avoid contamination of the surface.

FRICTION

Slip is the ability of two pieces of the same film to slide over one another or of a piece of film to slide over a metal surface. Slip is one of the properties used to predict film machinability since it is a deficiency of this property that leads to sticking. This can be a serious problem on processing equipment.

Two methods are given in ASTM Standard D1894-63[73] for the measurement of coefficients of friction of plastic films. Procedure A, designated the "Stationary Sled, Moving Plane Procedure," and Procedure B, the "Moving Sled, Stationary Plane Procedure." In both methods, one covers the surface of the plane with the film to be tested and also wraps the sled (a metal block covered with sponge rubber) with the same film. The sled is placed on the plane and, in Procedure A, the sled is attached to a spring which measures the frictional force when the plane is moved at a constant rate of speed. The static coefficient is determined by taking the scale reading when the initial sliding takes place and the kinetic coefficient by taking the reading after sliding is initiated. The recommended speed and block weight should be used since the coefficient depends on these quantities.

In Procedure B the plane remains stationary and the sled is pulled at a uniform speed for the kinetic coefficient of friction. Certain types of polyethylene have film-film coefficients as low as .1, but slip additives can affect this property appreciably.

A somewhat different method uses an inclined plane.[74] The film is taped to the plane and a sled wrapped with the same material is placed on the incline. The plane is then tilted until the block just begins to slide (for the static coefficient of friction) or until the sled slides down the plane at constant speed (for the kinetic coefficient of friction). The coefficient obtained from this test does not depend very strongly on block weight. Results of the inclined plane method were compared to those of the stationary sled, moving plane method and found to check very well. However, the inclined-plane method cannot be used with very tacky materials for which the coefficient of friction is above 3.

Still another approach to measuring friction is based on a method originally developed for fibers.[75] A drum is covered with the film to be tested and a strip of film is draped over the drum as shown in Figure 4.15. One end of the strip is weighted and the other is attached to a

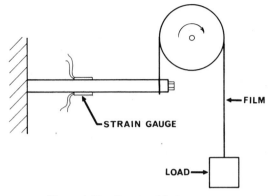

Figure 4.15.   Capstan friction tester.

strain gauge. When the drum is rotated, the frictional force is recorded by the strain gauge. Considerable difficulty may be encountered in applying this method to soft, extensible films.

Where the coefficient of friction between two different films is determined, it should be noted that the coefficient may vary depending on whether the plastic being tested is the static member or the moving member.[76]

Hand slip tests have been used for qualitative characterization. Like many qualitative tests, however, they have proven unsatisfactory for the most part because they are of little use in comparing films over extended periods of time.

WETTABILITY

This property is of most importance for polyolefins because these are not easily wetted. In order for ink to adhere to a film, it must wet the film surface. Normally polyolefin film that is to be printed is electrostatically or flame treated to improve wettability and, consequently, ink adhesion. Therefore, treatment level and ink adhesion tests are included in this section.

ASTM Standard D2578-67[77] provides a method for measuring wetting tension. Drops of solutions of increasing surface tension are applied to the film until a solution is found which just wets the surface. The surface tension of this mixture is taken to be the wetting tension of the film.

Another simple test for wettability of treated surfaces is used.[78] A specified volume of water is placed on a film surface and the area covered by the water is used as a measure of wettability: the larger the area covered, the more wettable is the surface.

Yet another way to determine wettability is to measure the contact angle formed between the film and a drop of liquid resting on it.[79] A 0° contact angle means complete wetting. In the cited paper a correlation is given between contact angle of a drop of *water* and ink adhesion.

Finally, wettability is found by measuring the angle at which a drop of water will start moving down a plane.[80,81] More specifically, a drop is placed on a supported horizontal plane surface covered with the film to be tested. The plane is tilted slowly and the angle at which the drop begins to slide is observed. Controlled temperature and relative humidity, as well as a clean surface, are important for reproducible results.

The "adhesion ratio" of polyethylene film is defined as the ratio of force required to peel a pressure-sensitive adhesive tape from a treated surface to the force required to peel similar tape from an untreated reference surface. The detailed experimental procedure for carrying out this test is given in ASTM Tentative D2141-63T.[82] The usefulness of this test lies in the fact that it has been observed that the force necessary to peel a tape from a treated surface correlates quite well with the degree of ink adhesion to this surface.

A simple test specifically used to measure treatment level is the dye-stain test.[83] The specimen to be tested is dipped in a certain dye which stains a treated surface but not an untreated one. The sample is removed and dried in a vertical position. Areas which show no staining have not been treated sufficiently.

Several tests are available and in use for measuring the adhesion of dried ink to a film.[83] In the "Scotch-tape"* test, a strip of tape is applied to the inked area. One end of the tape is gripped and manually pulled back at an angle of almost 180°. Pulling is done at a slow rate for about half the length of the inked region and then more rapidly for the remainder. The amount of ink removed by the tape is a measure of ink adhesion. This is a semi-quantitative test at best. The test is not very precise since ink adhesion will depend on the pressure used to apply the tape to the inked area, the rate at which the tape is peeled from the inked area, and the variation from roll to roll of the pressure-sensitive tape, among other things. Also, overtreatment cannot be detected with this test.

Commercial Standard CS-227-59 (U.S. Department of Commerce) describes a similar test in which the pull is not applied by hand but rather by a mechanical force.

* Registered trade name.

In another ink-adhesion test,[84] ink is applied to the film in a standard manner, dried and the base of an ordinary bottle cork is secured to the ink by an adhesive. The cork serves merely as a "handle" to be gripped by a tensile tester. The adhesion tester pulls in a direction perpendicular to the plane of the film and the force needed to break the ink-film bond is determined. Of course, for this method to work properly the bond between cork-adhesive and adhesive-ink must be stronger than that between ink and film.

BIOLOGICAL RESISTANCE

Films prepared from polymers containing additives such as plasticizers or stabilizers are often subject to fungus attack. ASTMD1924-63[85] recommends a procedure to be followed for determining the resistance of plastics to fungi. The test piece is inoculated with appropriate organisms and then exposed to conditions favoring their growth. After a suitable time, changes in visual appearance are observed, and standard tests are made on the sample, for example, tensile strength or haze, in order to ascertain the effect of the fungus.

Bacterial resistance of film is measured by placing a film between micro-organisms and solid media (in contact with the film) and using the growth on solid media as an indication of penetration.[86,87] After suitable sterilization, the film can also be tested for any deterioration in physical properties such as tensile strength.

An insect penetration test[88] has also found some use. The test specimen separates two chambers. Food is placed in the lower chamber. The upper chamber contains 50 adult insects. The film is examined periodically for penetration by the insects.

FLATNESS

Flatness is one of those properties mentioned earlier which is usually of much more consequence during the processing of a film than in its end use; "bag," "bag and sag," and "dogleg" are among the terms used to indicate a lack of flatness.

As a preliminary to following the test procedure given in ASTM Standard D1604-63,[89] two parallel straight lines are drawn on a table 100 inches apart and perpendicular to an edge of that table. In conducting the test, the film is spread out on the table and adjusted so that its edges are parallel to the table edge and the film ends cover the two parallel lines. The sheet is smoothed out as much as possible and the sample is cut to a length of 100 inches using the two parallel lines as guides. Two-inch-wide strips are then cut from both edges, the center, and any wrinkled sections. The length of each strip is measured using a minimum of tension to remove wrinkles, and the difference between this figure and 100 inches is designated as the percentage out-of-flatness for that strip. If a sample is stated to have an out-of-flatness of .9, this means that the *maximum* length of any of the two-inch-wide strips is 100.9 inches.

Essentially what are measured in this test are differences in fiber* lengths. These differences are important because they induce wrinkling as the longer fibers adjust to the length of the shortest in a piece of machinery. It is characteristic of this test that flatness is measured under practically no tension and thus, in a sense, shows the out-of-flatness in the worst possible light.

Since this test takes 10 to 20 minutes to complete (depending on the number of strips that are cut and the nature of the film), flatness may actually change during the test due to shrinkage which occurs even at room temperature for films of certain polymers.

A modification to the ASTM procedure consists of cutting lengthwise two-inch-wide strips across the *entire width* of the sheet. The lengths of these strips are measured just as before. A graph is then made of length-of-strip versus position across the film. The result is a flatness profile (see Figure 4.16).

It will be noted that the change from the ASTM test is not so much in the mechanics of the test as in the treatment of data generated by the test. This modification is important because in many cases, particularly when the test is used as a research tool, it is necessary to know *where* the short fibers are concentrated and similarly for the long fibers. Strips narrower than two inches wide may be cut for a more accurate profile, but the testing time required goes up accordingly.

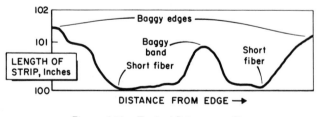

Figure 4.16.   Typical flatness profile.

---

* The film is imagined to be composed of an infinite number of fibers extending the length of the film and of "diameter" equal to the thickness of the film.

To repeat, the flatness tests described above measure the out-of-flatness under almost no tension. In actual use, film is generally under some tension so that it may be more realistic to measure the flatness as a function of tension or at least at some specified non-zero tension. This can be accomplished by mounting the film in a clamp, passing it over a roll, and weighting the free end as shown in Figure 4.17. The "sag" at P can be measured with a probe, as a function of position across the web, using an appropriate reference line.

Further refinements include sag measurements at various temperatures.

ODOR

It has been customary in the past to rate the odor levels of films by a panel of human testers. The odor of the test specimen is compared to the odor of some standard material, a scale of numbers being provided to indicate the intensity of odor. For example, given a scale running from one to ten, the standard is assigned a value of five and the test specimens might take on any of the values up to and including ten.

Efforts are now being made to make more quantitative measurements of odor. It has been found that sensitivity to odor depends on the concentration of the odorous substance (as a vapor) and the force with which the air current strikes the odor-sensitive area of the nose. Therefore, as a first step toward objectivizing the measurement of odor, a test has been devised[90] in which the nose still remains as the detector, but the "sniff" is mechanized by blowing a fixed volume of the odorous air at a fixed rate into a nostril. The odor level is compared to that of a standard, which is also sniffed mechanically.

A somewhat more basic approach to quantifying odor measurement has also been made.[91] In this procedure odorous vapor is inserted into

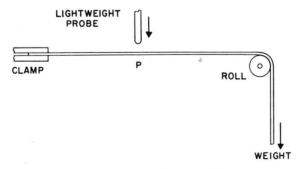

Figure 4.17.   Measurement of flatness under tension.

the head of a chromatographic column and an ionization detector used to analyze the components of the odor.

ORIENTATION AND SHRINKAGE

Orientation itself is not of primary practical importance but the way in which it affects the physical and mechanical properties of a film is of extreme importance, so that some brief remarks on its measurement are in order.

Two optical methods for measuring orientation are in fairly common use: birefringence and infrared dichroism. The birefringence method arose because it was found that the index of refraction is highly dependent on orientation. Birefringence is defined as the difference between the indices of refraction *in* the plane and *perpendicular* to the plane of the film and is taken as a measure of the orientation present in the film.

The method of infrared dichroism is based on the experimental result that absorption of incident polarized infrared radiation depends on how the polarization direction is oriented with respect to the molecular orientation in the film.

Experimental methods for measuring birefringence and infrared dichroism of thin films have been published.[92,93]

Like refractive index, the speed of sound varies with orientation level in oriented films. A device has been developed to measure the speed of sound in oriented fibers and films.[94] When it is perfected, this device may be of considerable value in process control, since the test is nondestructive and capable of giving instantaneous readings on oriented samples.

An ASTM Standard, D1504-61,[95] can be followed to measure the "orientation release stress" in a plastic film. The film strip is clamped in two grips (under no tension), one of which is attached to a force measuring device. The temperature is now raised to a specified level, and the maximum force developed due to retractive stresses is recorded.

Change in dimensions of plastic materials may be caused by creep (deformation under load), swelling or shrinkage due to absorption or loss of moisture, and shrinkage which accompanies the relief of internal stresses at elevated temperatures. The latter source of dimensional change is the most common for films. The internal stresses are mainly those frozen in during the orientation process. ASTM Standard D1204-54[96] is the relevant standard test. The test specimen is cut with the aid of a square template to a standard size. The specimen is marked to show the machine direction and is placed between two sheets of heavy paper and then inserted into a mechanical convection oven at a pre-selected temperature and for a time period appropriate to the film being tested. At the end of the testing period the specimen is removed from the oven, and the linear dimensional changes are obtained from measurements made on the shrunk sample. The linear change,

$$\% = \frac{d_t - d_i}{d_i} \times 100$$

where d_t = final length and d_i = initial length. A negative value denotes shrinkage and a positive value indicates expansion. Many published tables are compiled in terms of "shrinkage"; in such tables, a positive value denotes shrinkage and a negative value indicates expansion.

The main characteristic of this test is that it measures the *un-restrained* dimensional change of a film and this should be kept in mind when using the test to predict shrink packaging behavior.

The specification is silent on the question of length of time that the film is to be heated. One way of specifying this time is to determine the dimensional change as a function of time at a given temperature, plot these results and note where this curve levels off. The time where this occurs is taken as the appropriate time period for future tests. In some cases this may not be possible because of problems with degradation.

A variation of the ASTM test involves immersion of the sample to be tested in an inert hot liquid bath. For example, oriented polystyrene film can be shrunk in hot glycerin without adverse side effects. The time required to achieve a given degree of shrinkage at a fixed temperature is naturally much less in a hot liquid bath than in a hot-air oven because of the more favorable heat transfer from the liquid medium.

By clamping opposite edges of a rectangular specimen and leaving the other two edges free, one can obtain the shrinkage behavior of film restrained in one direction. For some oriented films at least, when film is restrained in the machine direction, the shrinkage in the transverse direction is much higher than in a free shrinkage experiment. This type of test may be much more meaningful than free shrinkage tests, since in most shrink applications or processes, the film is partially restrained in some way.

IDENTIFICATION OF FILMS

Positive identification of plastic films is a relatively lengthy and complex operation. However, some simple tests can be made on a specimen which will reduce the number of possibilities and enable a reasonable guess to be made as to its nature. Two published articles[97,98] outline several simple tests which can be made, among them: stretching, shrinking, burning, heating, solubility, density.

A sample can be classified as to extensibility by hand stretching it. A nonextensible film such as polystyrene has an elongation-at-break of less than 25%; highly extensible films such as polyethylene may have elongations of several hundred percent. By this same test a sample can be tested for isotropy of mechanical properties.

If the sample of film is held in a flame and shrinks appreciably, the film was stretched (oriented) during its manufacture. In this way the film can be classed as oriented or nonoriented.

In the halogen (chlorine, fluorine) test, the sample is melted onto a hot copper wire and this wire is then held in the outer portion of a Bunsen flame. If the flame turns green, this indicates the presence of a halogen and, consequently, the specimen could be polyvinyl chloride but not polystyrene.

If a sample is placed in the bottom of a test tube and heated, observations of the film during the entire heating process may give some useful clues as to its identity. The fumes given off can be analyzed with litmus paper to indicate whether acids or alkalis are present.

A simple solubility test can also be used to categorize a film. A small piece of film is placed in a given solvent and agitated periodically. Whether the sample dissolves, swells, or is unaffected can indicate what polymer is involved.

Tables are provided in each of the cited references, which show reactions to the above tests for many common polymeric materials.

The density of a specimen can be easily measured in a density gradient column according to ASTM Standard D1505-67,[99] although for thin films the time required to reach an equilibrium level in the column may be several hours. An alternative method[100] measures refractive indices in the machine, transverse and thickness directions, and converts the average of these into a density value. Film densities can be measured in minutes by this technique.

THICKNESS MEASUREMENT

First, a few words about units follow. Film thicknesses are most commonly expressed in "mils" (.001 in. = 1 mil) or "gauge" (.00001 in. = 1 gauge), but occasionally other units are used. The following table will permit conversions among these units:

to go from	to	multiply by
gauge	mils	.01
millimeters (mm)	mils	39.37
microns (μ)	mils	.03937

Undoubtedly the simplest measuring device for thin film and sheet is the dial micrometer. The apparent thickness as measured by this instrument is dependent upon the pressure exerted by the foot and the nonparallelism of the foot and table. Furthermore, this instrument is not suited for continuous measurements. Despite these deficiencies, it remains practically indispensable for rapid, "batchwise" measurements.

The beta ray gauge has received much attention in recent years.[101] The principle can be understood by reference to Figure 4.18. Electrons from a radioactive source A pass into the film B, and some are transmitted and some are absorbed. The detector C measures the amount transmitted. The amount of radiation absorbed depends on the mass, but for materials of constant density this dependence can be transformed to thickness. The instrument is well-suited for continuous thickness measurements, in which case the source and detector are frequently disposed so that they traverse the film. In Figure 4.18 the source and detector would move perpendicular to the plane of the paper. Sensitivities down to .01 mil are attainable.

Another means of continuously measuring the thickness of a moving plastic film is shown in Figure 4.19. Film A is passed between the plates B of a capacitor which is part of a tuned circuit. As the film thickness varies, it alters the resonant frequency of the grid circuit and thus

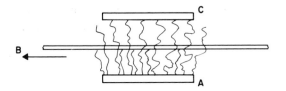

Figure 4.18.   Principle of a beta-ray gauge.

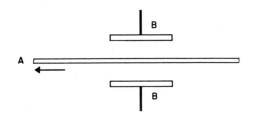

Figure 4.19.   Measurement of film thickness by capacitance change.

causes the plate current of the oscillator to vary. The change in plate current is amplified and recorded on a meter or continuously on a chart. The chart or meter can be calibrated to give the thickness in inches directly. Sensitivity is in the range of .01 mil. Note that there is no film contact with the measuring head. A dry film is necessary in order to utilize this device.

A method of measurement which gives an average thickness may be sufficient in many cases. The average thickness is obtained by weighing a standard-size specimen of the film in question and calculating the average thickness (or "weight gauge") by the following formula.

$$t = \frac{6100\,W}{\mathrm{dlw}}$$

W = Weight of the test specimen, grams.

l, w = Length and Width of the test piece, inches.

d = Density of the film, grams/cc.

t = Gauge.

By using a standard-size sample and assuming the density of a given film to be constant, the average thickness is easily calculated from the above formula, since it is then directly proportional to the weight. ASTM Standard E252-67[102] deals with substantially the same technique.

YIELD

The term "yield" in plastics film terminology usually means the number of square inches of film contained in one pound. It is sometimes referred to as the "area factor." Yield can be calculated from the formula

$$Y = \frac{27660}{dt}$$

where d is the film density in grams per cc and t is the film thickness in mils. The use of the average thickness (weight gauge) rather than an individual measurement obtained with a micrometer may be advisable for more reliability.

In conclusion, testing methods have been developed to measure the most pertinent film properties to almost any desired degree of precision. These measurements correlate sufficiently well, in many instances, with actual film performance, that little more is needed by way of analysis. In other instances, where the end use may involve complex laminates or complicated applications, measures of single properties still do not correlate well with performance. In these cases the protective packaging material still has to be evaluated in the actual end use. Thus, there is still much room for improvements in testing procedures, and we can expect to see activity continuing at a high level in test development work aimed at simplifying the users' selection of packaging materials.

The profusion of new plastic film and sheet materials that have been developed in the last few years dramatizes this need for more sophisticated testing to enable users to more precisely evaluate cost versus performance in the selection of new materials for field applications. This close analysis of properties can even point the way to novel applications. For instance, the outstanding resistance to ultraviolet degradation shown by polyvinyl fluoride led directly to its use as a permanent siding finish. This is an application in which plastic materials could not previously compete.

We can expect to continue to reap benefits from the continuing development of more sophisticated and varied test procedures in the future.

REFERENCES

1. *1968 Book of ASTM Standards*, Part 27, 780.
2. *1968 Book of ASTM Standards*, Part 27, 492.
3. Major, C. J., *Mod. Packaging*, **36**, No. 5, 119 (January, 1963).
4. Major, C. J., and Kammermeyer, K., *Mod. Plastics*, **39**, No. 11, 135 (July, 1962).
5. Filson, A. C., and Holmes-Walker, W. A., *Plastics*, **26**, No. 280, 117 (February, 1961).
6. Fricke, H. L., *Package Engineering*, **7**, No. 12, 51 (December, 1962).
7. Taylor, A. A., Karel, M., and Proctor, B. E., *Mod. Packaging*, **33**, No. 10, 131 (June, 1960).
8. Bredeweg, R. L., and Caldecourt, V. J., 14th Annual Conference on Mass Spectrometry and Allied Topics, Dallas, Texas (May 23, 1966).
9. *1968 Book of ASTM Standards*, Part 27, 815.
10. Lelchuk, S. L., and Sedlis, V. I., *J. of Appl. Chem. (USSR)*, English translation, **30**, No. 7, 1106 (July, 1957).
11. Doty, P. M., Aiken, W. H., and Mark, H., *Ind. Eng. Chem.* (Analytical Edition), **16**, No. 11, 686 (November, 1944).
12. Sivadjian J., and Corral, F., *J. Appl. Polymer Sci.*. **6**, No. 23, 561 (September–October, 1962).
13. Ranger, H. O., and Gluckman, M. J., *Mod. Packaging*, **37**, No. 11, 153 (July, 1964).
14. Amdur, E. J., *Mod. Plastics*, **40**, No. 16, 141 (December, 1967).
15. Ninnemann, K. W., and Simerl, L. E., *Mod. Packaging*, **35**, No. 4, 137 (December, 1961).

16. *1968 Book of ASTM Standards*, Part 27, 159.
17. *1968 Book of ASTM Standards*, Part 27, 487.
18. *1968 Book of ASTM Standards*, Part 27, 152.
19. *1968 Book of ASTM Standards*, Part 27, 465.
20. *1968 Book of ASTM Standards*, Part 15, 190.
21. Burgman, H. A., and Calderwood, R. H., *Mod. Plastics*, **41**, No. 11, 143 (July, 1964).
22. Davis, E. G., Karel, M., and Proctor, B. E., *Mod. Packaging*, **33**, No. 4, 135 (December, 1959).
23. *1968 Book of ASTM Standards*, Part 27, 690.
24. Wormald, D., *Brit. Plastics*, **31**, No. 9, 392 (September, 1958).
25. *1968 Book of ASTM Standards*, Part 26, 237.
26. Spangler, R. D., and Cooper, E. B., *J. Appl. Phys.*, **28**, No. 3, 329 (March, 1957).
27. McMillan, J. G., *Mod. Packaging*, **27**, No. 12, 119 (August, 1954).
28. Amborski, L. E., and Mecca, T. D., *J. Appl. Polymer Sci.*, **4**, No. 12, 332 (November–December, 1960).
29. Patterson, Jr., G. D., and Miller, Jr., W. H., *J. Appl. Polymer Sci.*, **4**, No. 12, 291 (November–December, 1960).
30. Carey, R. H., and Nutkis, M. S., *Mod. Packaging*, **32**, No. 1, 147 (September, 1958).
31. Vincent, P. I., *Plastics*, **27**, No. 295, 133 (May, 1962).
32. Westover, R. F., and Warner, W. C., *Mater. Res. Std.*, **1**, No. 11, 867 (November, 1961).
33. Wolstenholme, W. E., *J. Appl. Polymer Sci.*, **6**, No. 21, 332 (May–June, 1962).
34. Dunn, T., and Kelly, P., *SPE J*, **20**, No. 7, 615 (July, 1964).
35. Glyde, B. S., Holmes-Walker, W. A., and Jeffs, K. D., *Brit. Plastics*, **34**, No. 8, 432 (August, 1961).
36. Conti, J., *Mod. Packaging*, **37**, No. 8, 216 (April, 1964).
37. *1968 Book of ASTM Standards*, Part 27, 578.
38. *1968 Book of ASTM Standards*, Part 27, 431.
39. *1968 Book of ASTM Standards*, Part 27, 235.
40. *1968 Book of ASTM Standards*, Part 27, 468.
41. Brownlee, R. N., *Pulp and Paper*, **29**, No. 11, 130 (October, 1955).
42. Hansen, Jr., O. C., Marker, L., Ninnemann, K. W., and Sweeting, O. J., *Mod. Packaging*, **36**, No. 6, 121 (February, 1963).
43. Noll. R. G., and Teeple, J. H., *Mod. Packaging*, **36**, No. 11, 127 (July, 1963).
44. *1968 Book of ASTM Standards*, Part 27, 417.
45. Stackhouse, N., *Brit. Plastics*, **34**, No. 1, 34 (January, 1961).
46. *1968 Book of ASTM Standards*, Part 27, 643.
47. *1968 Book of ASTM Standards*, Part 27, 669.
48. *1968 Book of ASTM Standards*, Part 27, 768.
49. Reinhart, F. W., Brown, C., Boor, L., and Lamb, J. J., *ASTM Bulletin*, No. 210, 50 (December, 1955).
50. *1968 Book of ASTM Standards*, Part 27, 649.

51. *1968 Book of ASTM Standards*, Part 27, 364.
52. Dahlquist, C. A., Hendricks, J. O., and Taylor, N. W., *Ind. Eng. Chem.*, **43**, No. 6, 1404 (June, 1951).
53. Patterson, Jr., G. D., *Mater. Res. Std.*, **4**, No. 4, 159 (April, 1964).
54. Hopkins, I. L., Baker, W. O., and Howard, J. B., *J. Appl. Phys.*, **21**, No. 3, 206 (March, 1950).
55. McKelvey, J. M., and Strome, T. H., *Mod. Plastics*, **36**, No. 10 (June, 1959).
56. *1968 Book of ASTM Standards*, Part 27, 751.
57. Knittel, R. R., *Mater. Res. Std.*, **2**, No. 3, 180 (March, 1962).
58. *1968 Book of ASTM Standards*, Part 27, 409.
59. Clegg, P. L., and Huck, N. D., *Plastics*, **26**, No. 282, 114 (April, 1961).
60. Henderson, W. E., Sacks, W., Lindenmeyer, P. H., and Morton, G. H., in Renfrew, A., and Morgan, P., Ed., *Polythene*, Interscience Publishers, 1960, 660.
61. Hay, P. M., Evans, C. P., and Ninnemann, K. W., *Mod. Packaging*, **33**, No. 3, 179 (November, 1959).
62. Webber, A. C., *J. Opt. Soc. Am.*, **47**, No. 9, 785 (September, 1957).
63. *1968 Book of ASTM Standards*, Part 27, 575.
64. Binsbergen, F. L., and VanDuijn, J., *J. Appl. Polymer Sci.*, **11**, No. 10, 1915 (October, 1967).
65. Miles, J. A. C., and Thornton, A. E., *Brit. Plastics*, **35**, No. 1, 26 (January, 1962).
66. *1968 Book of ASTM Standards*, Part 27, 594.
67. Hendrickson, T. C., *Mod. Packaging*, **40**, No. 13, 171 (September, 1967).
68. Lever, A. E. and Rhys, J., *The Properties and Testing of Plastic Materials*, 2nd Edition, Chemical Publishing Co., Inc., 185 (1962).
69. Tremain, H. E., *Plastics Technol.*, **9**, No. 3, 38 (March, 1963).
70. Shashoua, V. E., *J. Polymer Sci.*, **33**, No. 126, 65 (December, 1958).
71. Langdon, S. J., *Plastics*, **29**, No. 322, 43 (August, 1964).
72. Weston, D., *Plastics*, **24**, No. 265, 465 (November, 1959).
73. *1968 Book of ASTM Standards*, Part 27, 598.
74. Egan, W., *Mod. Packaging*, **29**, No. 4, 143 (December, 1955).
75. Owens, D. K., *J. Appl. Polymer Sci.*, **8**, No. 3, 1465 (May–June, 1964).
76. Anon., *Plastics*, **26**, No. 281, 117 (March, 1961).
77. *1968 Book of ASTM Standards*, Part 26, 730.
78. Taylor, P. A., *The Plastics Institute, Transactions and Journal*, **32**, No. 105, 53 (June, 1965).
79. Allan, A. J. G., *J. Polymer Sci.*, **38**, No. 134, 297 (August, 1959).
80. Kawasaki, K., *J. Colloid Sci.*, **15**, No. 5, 402 (October, 1960).
81. Baer, E., and McLaughlin, T. F., *J. Appl. Polymer Sci.*, **5**, No. 14, 240 (March–April, 1961).
82. *1968 Book of ASTM Standards*, Part 26, 378.
83. Smith, E. A., *SPE Tech. Papers, VIII, (ANTEC)*, Paper No. 13–2, (January 30–February 2, 1962).
84. Throne, J. M., *Mod. Plastics*, **42**, No. 10, 144 (June, 1965).
85. *1968 Book of ASTM Standards*, Part 27, 653.

86. *1968 Book of ASTM Standards*, Part 26, 840.
87. Griffin, R. G., Nosrati, M. H., Lampi, R. A., and Szczeblowski, J. S., *Mod. Packaging*, **40**, No. 14, 164 (October, 1967).
88. Gerhardt, P. D., and Lindgren, D. L., *Mod. Packaging*, **28**, No. 8, 216 (April, 1955).
89. *1968 Book of ASTM Standards*, Part 26, 159.
90. Clausen, D. F., Felt, C. E., Borchardt, L. F., and Reinsch, A. A., *Mod. Packaging*, **29**, No. 3, 149 (November, 1955).
91. Mackay, D. A. M., Lang, D. A., and Berdick, M., *Anal. Chem.*, **33**, No. 10, 1369 (September, 1961).
92. Stein, R. S., *J. Polymer Sci.*, **24**, No. 107, 383 (May, 1957).
93. Stein, R. S., *J. Appl. Polymer Sci.*, **5**, No. 13, 96 (January–February, 1961).
94. H. M. Morgan Company, 3 Pacific Street, Cambridge, Massachusetts.
95. *1968 Book of ASTM Standards*, Part 26, 119.
96. *1968 Book of ASTM Standards*, Part 27, 451.
97. Bird, V., *Plastics Tech.*, **9**, No. 9, 40 (September, 1963).
98. Johnson, R. C., and Sauber, W. J., *Western Plastics* (January 1959).
99. *1968 Book of ASTM Standards*, Part 27, 518.
100. Schael, G. W., *J. Appl. Polymer Sci.*, **8**, No. 6, 2717 (November–December, 1964).
101. Gerhard, G., *SPE J.*, **17**, No. 11, 1173 (November, 1961).
102. *1968 Book of ASTM Standards*, Part 27, 842.

FIVE

physical properties of plastic films

L. S. MOUNTS

INTRODUCTION

Plastic films are used for packaging, construction, and industrial applications. Each end use or application requires a film with a particular set of properties to perform the functions of package fabrication, product protection, containment, and appearance or display. Other properties are sometimes required for industrial applications where the film becomes a functional part of the design.

Film properties may be broadly classified as physical, mechanical, chemical, optical, and thermal, with other subjective values such as machinability and printability. The physical properties include thickness, density, yield, water absorption, and flatness. The mechanical properties include tensile strength, elongation, modulus, impact strength, and slip or coefficient of friction. Chemical resistance, water vapor transmission rate (WVTR), and gas permeability are listed as chemical properties. Optical properties include transparency, haze, and gloss. Flammability, range of service temperatures, shrink, and heat sealing are thermal properties. Electrical properties are important for some industrial applications and include dielectric strength, dielectric constant, and loss factors. A discussion of test methods is found in Chapter 4.

The mechanical and thermal properties of plastic films are important factors in the fabrication of packages. Relatively low elongation and high slip are required for bag making. Bags can be fabricated using lap seals, fin seals, or side welding. Hot bar, impulse, hot wire, and dielectric sealers are used as well as adhesives. Plastic films with wide heat seal temperature ranges and low shrink levels can be sealed by the hot bar or hot wire techniques, while those that are oriented and shrink, require impulse or dielectric sealing. Form-fill-seal bag making equipment has the same sealing requirements as bag machines, but higher slip and less elongation are required in the film so it will form and feed properly.

Films with higher modulus (greater stiffness) and medium slip are used on overwrap machines. The stiffness is required for film feeding, and the medium slip level is necessary to ensure a tight wrap that doesn't wrinkle or distort. New packaging machine designs make it possible to utilize thinner and softer films than previously possible. Sealers with release coatings, Teflon belts, or hot point sealers make heat sealing possible with a wide range of films.

Thermoforming is required for skin and blister packaging, so heat stable sheets that have good hot strength and forming characteristics are required. Skin packaging materials should have high impact strength and puncture resistance. Blister packs are usually rigid and materials with a high tensile modulus are required. Good optical properties are required for both applications.

The package must provide different protective properties for different product types. Baked goods require a low moisture vapor transmission rate (MVTR) and resistance to greases and oils. A low MVTR is required for all types of candy packaging, and grease and oil resistance are also needed for chocolates. Bags for hard candy need good impact strength and resistance to puncturing. Cheese, other dairy products, and processed meats need low MVTR, low oxygen permeability, and good resistance to grease and oils. Fresh meat and fresh produce on the other hand require films that are permeable to gases. Frozen foods and boil-in-bag items need packages with good low temperature impact strength and moisture protection. The boil-in-bag also requires heat resistance to withstand the effects of boiling water during food preparation. Toys, hardware, housewares, and paper goods in general require high clarity, high impact strength films. Many of these items are skin or blister packaged and displayed on racks, so that excellent clarity is essential. Shrink packaging is also used for toys, hardware, paper goods and records. Tobacco needs moisture protection for freshness, but the film should have moderate transmission properties. One of the requirements of packaging films for tobacco and candy is high speed machinability.

For various industrial applications, high strength, temperature resistance, chemical resistance, or electrical properties are required. Examples are films used for electrical insulation, dielectrics in capacitors, liners for tanks and drums, diaphragms for chemical pumps and valves, and gasketing materials.

The functions of a package are to contain the product, protect it, display it in the store, and in many cases provide a use function as the product is consumed. In order to contain the product, the packaging film has to be machinable and sealable, have sufficient mechanical strength to withstand handling and shipping, and chemical resistance to retain its mechanical properties. To protect the product, mechanical properties are also required as well as the proper permeability factors and chemical resistance. Optical properties, printability, and dimensional stability are requirements for good appearance. Use factors can include good low temperature properties for frozen or refrigerated products, high temperature resistance for products that are sterilized or heated in the package, and mechanical strength for multi-use packages that are opened and then stored for future use.

The properties of a plastic film are functions of the chemical composition of the base polymer, the additives used, the formulation, the method of manufacture of the film, and post treatments or coatings. The basic film properties come from the chemical structure of the resin. The addition of plasticizers usually increases elongation, flexibility, and permeability, but lowers the maximum use temperature. Cast films usually have excellent optical properties, little heat distortion, and good gauge and flatness. Extruded films have greater mechanical strength than cast films. Oriented films have significantly greater mechanical strength and slightly reduced permeability rates, but will shrink at elevated temperatures. Post-treatments and coatings are used to improve ink adhesion, slip, barrier properties, heat stability, and sealing. Structured films and laminates take advantage of the properties of two or more materials to improve the overall properties of the structure.

The following section will outline the general properties of the different plastic film families and discuss some of these applications. Tables are included showing typical film properties.

THE CELLULOSICS

The cellulosics are derived from one of the most widely distributed and most readily available chemical raw materials, cellulose. The two most important sources of cellulose today are cotton linters and wood pulp. Cellulose is chemically converted to regenerated cellulose (rayon, cellophane), cellulose ethers (ethyl cellulose, methyl cellulose), and cellulose esters (cellulose nitrate, cellulose acetate, cellulose acetatebutyrate, etc.).

The chemical structure of cellulose is a repeating chain of anhydroglucose units.

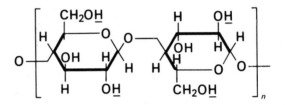

In producing cellulose acetate some of the underlined hydrogens ($\underline{H}$) are replaced by acetate groups ($-OCCH_3$). For ethyl cellulose and methyl cellulose the substitution is $-CH_2CH_3$ and $-CH_3$ respectively. Cellophane has the same structural formula as cellulose, but the original cellulose is treated with sodium hydroxide and carbon disulfide to form a soluble xanthate. The resulting solution or viscose is allowed to ripen in preparation for regeneration back to cellulose after casting into the desired form.

Cellophane.   Cellophane is produced by casting viscose solution onto a drum or belt in sheet form and coagulating it into a hard film. This results in a clear, nonthermoplastic base sheet. Cellophane has basic properties of clarity, heat stability, stiffness, and water absorbency. When dry, it has excellent gas barrier, but it transmits moisture vapor and gas readily when wet. To get the required properties for packaging applications, a variety of surface coatings are used to make it moistureproof and heat sealable. These coatings are basically nitrocellulose, polyvinyl chloride, polyvinylidene chloride or polyethylene.

The earliest coatings were formulated lacquers of nitrocellulose to provide different levels of moistureproofness and heat sealability. The base film can be coated on both sides or one side only to allow wettability, which increases the gas transmission rate of the film when it is used to wrap fresh meat or produce.

The vinyl copolymer coated films have better barrier properties than those with nitrocellulose coatings, and the polyvinylidene chloride coatings have the lowest gas and moisture transmission rates. They also provide oil and grease resistance as well as heat sealability. Neither the vinyl-copolymer coated cellophane nor the polyvinylidene chloride coated cellophane will seal to nitrocellulose coated films, so they can be used for bundling articles previously overwrapped in nitrocellulose coated film without adhering to it in the heat seal areas.

Polyethylene coated cellophane is normally coated on one side only. This allows the uncoated side to absorb moisture and increases the oxygen transmission rate so that red meat will retain its red color and bloom, while the polyethylene provides good heat sealability.

Cellophane has been produced in the United States since 1924 and approximately 400 million pounds are used per year. With the varieties of coatings used more than 100 types are available. Uses are for packaging meat, produce, tobacco, baked goods, snack foods, and many nonfood items. It is used in bag form, as an overwrap, for form-fill-seal,

TABLE 5.1.   Cellophane Properties

Property	Nitrocellulose, lacquered	Polymer, coated	Polyethylene, coated
Thickness, mils	.9	.9	1.1
Specific gravity	1.40	1.44	1.2
Yield, sq in./lb	19,500	19,200	18,250
Tensile strength, psi	7–16,000	7–13,000	5,000 and over
Elongation, %	15–25	25–50	15–25
Heat sealing range, °F	200–300	225–350	230–300
WVTR, $\frac{gm}{100 \text{ sq in.}/24 \text{ hr/mil}}$	.2–1.0	.5–1.0	1.2 and up
Gas permeability	Variable	Very low	Variable
Resistance greases and oils	Impermeable	Impermeable	Less resistant
Machine performance	Excellent	Excellent	Excellent
Printability	Excellent	Excellent	Good
Sealing	Heat or adhesives	Heat or adhesives	Heat
Heat shrink	None	None	None

TABLE 5.2.   Cellophane Designations

	Avisco	duPont	Olin
Nitrocellulose lacquer			
Moistureproof heat seal	MSB	MSAD	MSAT
Moistureproof nonseal	M	MD	MT
Less moistureproof seal	DSB	LSAD	LSAT
Vinyl coating	R-18		
Polyvinylidene chloride coated	RS	K	V
			OX
Polyethylene coating	RE	K-205 Lam.	OF-18

and bundling. Due to its basic clarity, stiffness, and heat stable nature, coatings can be used to provide slip and barrier properties, and heat sealing ranges tailored to fit specific applications.

Cellulose Acetate. Cellulose acetate is produced by the acetylation of cellulose. It is used for producing fibers, for molding, and for film and sheeting material. Film and sheeting are produced by extrusion or solvent casting methods.

Cellulose acetate has high clarity, good toughness and impact strength and high permeability to gas and moisture vapor. It can be plasticized to alter its flexibility. As a film, it is widely used as a window in envelopes and boxes and as an overwrap for fresh produce. Due to its heat formability, clarity, and toughness, the sheet is especially suitable for high quality formed blisters for display packaging and as folded transparent carton lids. Other uses are in the graphic arts field and as a substrate for photographic emulsions.

Cellulose Acetate Butyrate. Cellulose acetate butyrate is produced by esterifying cellulose, using a combination of butyric and acetic acids. It is similar in properties to cellulose acetate but has higher impact strength. For this reason it is normally used for blister forming of parts where high strength is necessary, such as packaging of heavy hardware items.

Cellulose Propionate. This is one of the newer cellulosics. Propionic acid is used with cellulose to produce the ester. It is also used for forming applications.

Ethyl Cellulose. This is an ether of alkali cellulose and ethyl chloride. It can be produced in sheet form by either solvent casting or slot extrusion. Ethyl cellulose has properties similar to cellulose acetate but with greater toughness and flexibility, especially at low temperatures. Its uses are in formed blisters, folded carton lids, and for graphic arts.

POLYOLEFIN FILMS

Polyolefin and olefin copolymer films are used in larger volume than any other class of packaging film and account for more than 50% of the total tonnage of plastic films sold today. Their growth has been phenomenal since their introduction in the late 1940's. Low density

TABLE 5.3.   Properties of Cellulose Ester and Ether Film and Sheet

Property	Cellulose Acetate Film	Cellulose Acetate Sheet	Cellulose Acetate Butyrate	Cellulose Propionate	Ethyl Cellulose
Gauge, mils	1.0	5.0	5.0	5.0	5.0
Specific gravity	1.31	1.31	1.29	1.20	1.15
Yield, sq in./lb	21,500	4,300	4,500	4,600	4,700
Tensile strength, psi	9–12,000	8–10,000	7–9,000	5–6,000	7–9,000
Elongation, %	15–25	25–30	50–60	73–83	25–35
WVTR, $\overline{\dfrac{gm}{100 \text{ sq in.}/24 \text{ hr}/mil}}$	40–75	40–75	50	—	75
O_2 transmission $\dfrac{cc}{100 \text{ sq in.}/24 \text{ hr}/atm/mil}$	150–270	150–270	200	—	330
H_2O absorp., % (24 hr immersion)	8.5	4–6	—	2.7	7.5
Printability	Excellent	Excellent	Good	Good	Excellent
Sealing	Adhesive dielectric	Adhesive dielectric	Adhesive	Adhesive	Adhesive

polyethylene films account for more than 600 million pounds per year and constitute the largest segment of the polyolefin film market. The properties of high impact strength, good tear resistance, low temperature flexibility, heat sealability, low water vapor permeability, chemical inertness, good clarity, and low price have contributed to this large volume usage.

Polyethylene Films. *Polyethylene* $(—CH_2—CH_2—CH_2—CH_2—)_n$ resin is available in a wide range of densities. Films are produced by blown bubble, internal mandrel, and chill roll casting techniques. The film properties obtained will vary depending to some degree on the manufacturing conditions used with a particular resin.

Low density polyethylene films (.910–.925 gm/cc) have the highest impact strength, lowest modulus, lowest heat seal temperature, and higher permeability than the medium density (.926–.940 gm/cc) and high density (.941–.965 gm/cc) films. Blown films have greater impact strength and toughness than chill roll cast films, but usually poorer optical properties. Polyethylene film is used as an overwrap, in fabricated bags, on form-fill-seal bag machines, and in laminates. Due to the film's all around good properties, it is used for packaging a large variety of products. Among these are fresh produce where the clarity, low MVTR, high gas transmission rate, and toughness are important; frozen foods require cold temperature flexibility, impact strength, and low MVTR; baked goods require high clarity, low MVTR, good sealing and bag fabrication. Textiles and paper products take advantage of the toughness in thin gauges, ease of fabrication, clarity, soft feel, and low cost. Other important markets are meat and poultry, dry cleaning and laundry, carton liners, and a long list of miscellaneous uses.

Medium density polyethylene films have similar properties to low density films, but show higher clarity and greater stiffness. The greater stiffness improves the machinability for overwrap applications on the products listed above. High density polyethylene films are used where greater stiffness, tensile strength, chemical resistance, or heat stability are required. High density polyethylene finds its largest use in blown bottles. Polyethylene films also are used in many nonpackaging applications such as construction and agriculture. Typical properties of polyethylene films are listed in Table 5.4.

The impact strength, high temperature properties, and shrinkability of polyethylene films can be much improved by cross-linking induced with ionizing radiation. This allows normal extrusion and fabrication of

TABLE 5.4.   Typical Properties of Polyethylene Films

	Low density Polyethylene	Med. density Polyethylene	High density Polyethylene	Irradiated oriented Polyethylene
Density, gm/cc	.910–.925	.926–.940	.941–.965	.916–.924
Gauge, mil	1.0	1.0	1.0	.75
Yield, sq in./lb	30,000	29,500	29,000	40,000
Tensile strength, psi	1,800–2,700	2,000–3,500	3,000–10,000	9,000–16,000
Elongation, %	225–600	225–500	5–400	40–100
Tensile modulus, psi	28,000–32,000	40,000–50,000	120,000–150,000	50,000–60,000
WVTR, $\frac{gm}{100\ sq\ in./24\ hr/mil}$	1.2	1.0	.5	2.5
O_2 transmission rate, $\frac{cc}{100\ sq\ in./24\ hr/atm/mil}$	420	400	200	650
Service temp., °F	− 60 to 180	− 60 to 180	− 60 to 250	− 60 to 200
Heat seal temp., °F	260–350	270–350	290–370	350–400
Mach. performance	Fair–good	Good	Good	Fair
Printability	Good when treated	Good when treated	Good when treated	Fair
Heat shrink	Low in blown films	None	None	High

low density resins, with postirradiation increasing the molecular weight. Dosages up to 10 megarads are used. One use of such irradiated films is for shipping bags, where gauge can be reduced because of the increased toughness of the film. Polyethylene and copolymer films of ethylene and ethyl acrylate, acrylic acid, and vinyl acetate can be irradiated, then biaxially stretched to make improved impact strength shrink films. Applications are shrink wrapping, bundling, shrink bags, and as a fresh meat wrap.

POLYPROPYLENE FILMS

The chemical structure of polypropylene is as follows:

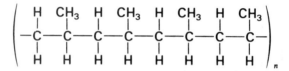

Polypropylene films were introduced to the packaging field during the 1950's. They have inherently greater stiffness, clarity, grease resistance, barrier properties, and a lower density than polyethylene films. Unoriented films are manufactured by chill roll casting. Below 32°F they become brittle due to their crystallinity and have a narrower heat sealing range than polyethylene films. Their main applications are as bread wrap and as twist wraps for candy.

Oriented polypropylene films are produced by stretching and heat setting the extruded films under controlled temperature conditions. Orientation increases the tensile strength, low temperature flexibility abrasion resistance, and barrier properties. It also makes the film heat shrinkable and narrows the sealing range. The orientation can be biaxial, giving balanced properties, or uniaxial, having the improved properties principally in one direction. Shrink films are sealed by special point sealers, hot wire, hot knife, or impulse. They find application for shrink wrapping of toys, games, records, and soft goods.

Oriented polypropylene films can be heat set by annealing. This reduces the shrink and improves the sealability. Applications are for bags, pouches, and bag liners. Heat set films are used in laminations and printing to provide stiffness, gloss, clarity, and scuff resistance. One main application is bags for snack foods when laminated to glassine or cellophane.

Heat set films can also be coated to increase slip and barrier and improve heat sealing. Typical coatings are polyethylene, polyvinyl acetate, ethylene-vinyl acetate copolymer or polyvinylidene chloride. These coated films are used for packaging bakery products, tobacco, and as windows in cartons and bags.

As new coatings are developed and base films with different properties are produced, more applications will open up to polypropylene films. They can be tailored to have properties similar to those of the different types of cellophane and with the advantages of greater strength and only slight changes in properties under widely varying humidity conditions. Since thinner gauges can be used due to greater unit strength, costs are potentially lower than for cellophane. Typical properties are listed in Table 5.5.

Ethylene Propylene Copolymers.   *Ethylene–propylene* (EP) copolymers are used to make films having a combination of the properties of film produced from the monomers. Block copolymer films with a small percentage of ethylene have better heat sealability, cold temperature flex, and impact strength than polypropylene films. This improvement is accomplished without orientation. The toughness and sealability of the EP films are similar to polyethylene, while the high clarity, stiffness, abrasion resistance, and barrier properties of polypropylene films are retained. These EP copolymers are a relatively new plastics development. Initial packaging applications include side weld bags for soft goods; produce and bakery bags; overwraps; and extrusion coating of paper for label and bag liner stock. Further properties are listed in Table 5.5.

Ethylene Copolymers.   Ethylene is copolymerized with other monomers to create resins with particular properties. Some property improvement has been achieved in the past by blending resins, but the films obtained from these blends were hazy. The copolymer films exhibit excellent clarity.

Ethylene-Vinyl Acetate.   Ethylene-vinyl acetate (EVA) copolymers offer a wide range of molecular weights and have the following structure:

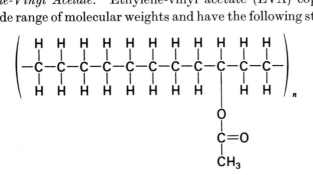

TABLE 5.5. Typical Properties of Polypropylene Films

Property	Unoriented Polypropylene film	Biaxially oriented Polypropylene film	Saran coated oriented Polypropylene	Ethylene-Propylene Copolymer
Density, gm/cc	.88–.90	.90	—	.90–.91
Gauge, mils	1.0	.70	.80	1.00
Yield, sq in./lb/mil	30,300	30,000	22–27,000	30,000
Tensile strength, psi	3,000–6,000	13,000–30,000	10,000–29,000	3,000–6,000
Elongation, %	200–500	40–200	40–300	300–600
Tensile modulus, psi	90,000–120,000	250,000–450,000	250,000–400,000	80,000–90,000
WVTR, $\dfrac{\text{gm}}{100 \text{ sq in./24 hr/mil}}$	.7	.4	.3	.8
O_2 transmission rate, $\dfrac{\text{cc}}{100 \text{ sq in./24 hr/atm/mil}}$	240	200	1–3	300
Service temperature, °F	32–310	– 30 to 250	– 30 to 250	– 30 to 250
Heat seal temperature, °F	260–310	260–270	200–270	240–290
Mach. performance	Good	Good	Good	Good
Printability	Good when treated	Yes	Yes	Yes
Heat shrink	None	Yes	Yes	None

The low molecular weight EVA resins are used for hot melts, wax modifiers, and as heat seal coatings. They can also be used in solvent systems for lacquers or modifiers for lacquers to improve their gloss and moisture barrier. The higher molecular weight copolymers can be extruded into film and usually contain 16–30% vinyl acetate by weight. EVA films have greater impact strength, a wider heat sealing range, and greater flexibility than low density polyethylene films, but poorer chemical resistance and less barrier to moisture and oxygen. EVA films are used in laminates to provide more flexible structures and a lower heat seal temperature.

Ethylene Ethyl Acrylate.   Ethylene ethyl acrylate (EEA) copolymers have the following structure:

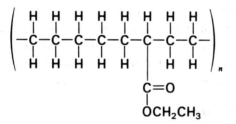

The EEA copolymers are more thermally stable than those of EVA and can be used in extrusion coating as the heat seal ply or to sandwich other webs together. EEA films have a tackier surface and poorer optical properties than EVA.

Ethylene Acrylic Acid.   Ethylene acrylic acid (EAA) copolymers have the following structure:

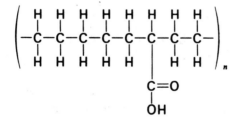

These copolymers have very strong adhesive properties and are used in applications where this is desirable. Strong bonds are possible with metals and fibrous materials using heat and pressure for laminating.

Ionomers.   Copolymers of ethylene and various unsaturated acids can be further reacted with a metal ion to produce a new class of resins known as "Ionomers".* A typical structure would be as follows:

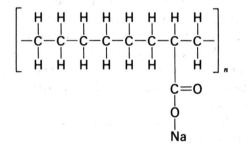

"Ionomer" films have excellent clarity and impact strength compared to low density polyethylene films. Because of this good clarity and impact strength, ionomer films are used for skin packaging and shrink wraps. They also provide improved oil and grease resistance and heat sealing properties when laminated to other substrates. Table 5.6 compares the properties of several ethylene copolymer films.

Halogenated Polymer Films

Polyvinyl Chloride.   Polyvinyl chloride (PVC) films and sheeting can have a broad range of properties depending on base resin, plasticizer content, and method of manufacture. Following the cellulosics and polyolefins, PVC is the third largest volume plastic film used in packaging and is the one that is growing most rapidly. Plasticizer contents can vary from 0–40% or more. Film and sheeting is produced by slot-die extrusion, calendering, bubble process, and solvent casting methods. The chemical structure of PVC is as follows:

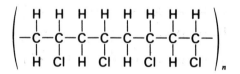

The general properties of PVC are good chemical resistance, good mechanical strength, and intermediate barrier properties. Plasticizer is added to improve flexibility and to make processing easier. Highly plasticized PVC film and sheet normally becomes brittle at low temperatures, however. Vinyl chloride is copolymerized with vinyl acetate and

* Registered Trade Mark.

TABLE 5.6.   Properties of Polyethylene and Ethylene Copolymer Films

	Low density Polyethylene	Ethylene Vinyl Acetate	Ethylene Ethyl Acrylate	Ethylene Acrylic Acid	"Ionomer"*
Density, gm/cc	.910–.925	.94	.93	.93	.94
Yield, sq in./lb/mil	30,000	29,400	29,600	30,000	29,400
Tensile strength, psi	1,800–2,700	1,400–3,800	800–2,000	1,300–3,300	3,500–5,500
Elongation, %	225–600	650–900	300–700	400–600	300–400
WVTR, $\dfrac{\text{gm}}{100 \text{ sq in./24 hr/mil}}$	1.2	1.8–3.0	1.4	1.3	1.5–2.5
O$_2$ transmission, $\dfrac{\text{cc}}{100 \text{ sq in./24 hr/atm/mil}}$	420	600–900	600–1,500	400	500

* Registered trade name.

other monomers to yield films that are flexible over a wider temperature range.

Thin plasticized PVC films are used for stretch wrapping of produce, fresh red meat, and soft goods. High clarity, medium to high transmission rate of moisture and gases, good flexibility, and high elongation combined with low cost are important properties for these applications. Oriented films are used for shrink wrapping of produce, fresh meat, soft goods, toys, and phonograph records. Heavier gauge, more rigid, oriented films are used for shrink bundling. In one application, oriented PVC film is used to bundle 24 cans of vegetables on a tray to replace the more usual corrugated shipping carton.

PVC sheet is used for blister and skin packaging of many items. Typical properties of various types of PVC film and sheet are listed in Table 5.7.

A large volume use of PVC sheet and film is not related to packaging. This is for shower curtains, inflatable toys, upholstery material, etc. This results from the wide range of properties, colors, and decoration possible because of PVC's compatibility with a great number of fillers, pigments, and plasticizers.

Polyvinylidene chloride.   Polyvinylidene chloride (PVDC) copolymer films are usually produced from copolymers of vinylidene chloride and vinyl chloride and have the following structure:

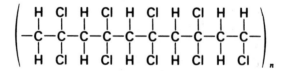

Film properties can be varied by changing the ratio of comonomers and the amount of additives in the resin. Films are produced by extrusion and oriented by a blown bubble process. Orientation increases flexibility, tensile strength, and low temperature toughness of films, made from saran resins.

The outstanding properties of PVDC films are their excellent chemical resistance and low moisture and gas transmission rates in clear film. PVDC films are resistant to oils, greases, and acids except concentrated nitric and sulfuric. They are also resistant to alcohols, aliphatic hydrocarbons, and organic acids. Tetrahydrofuran, aromatic ketones, and aliphatic ethers are about the only solvents which do attack the film. The tensile strength of the film is increased by orientation and ranges

TABLE 5.7. Typical Properties of PVC Film and Sheet

Property	Flexible Cast	Flexible Extruded	Flexible Oriented	Rigid Unoriented	Rigid Oriented
Specific gravity	1.27	1.32	1.30	1.38	1.38
Yield, sq in./lb/mil	23,000	21,500	22,000	19,500	19,500
Tensile strength, psi	4–6,000	4–10,000	15–19,000	7–10,000	6–14,000
Elongation, %	150–400	50–350	50–150	30–65	15–50
WVTR, gm/100 sq in. 24 hr/mil	10–20	6–15	5–7	.7	.7–3
O_2 transmission rate, cc 100 sq in./24 hr/atm/mil	600–900	35–100	30–100	6–12	8–14
Shrink	No	Some	Yes	No	Yes
Machinability	Fair	Fair	Fair	Good	Good

from 8,000–16,000 psi. Oriented PVDC films will shrink when exposed to temperatures above about 120°F. This shrinkability can be an advantage where a very tight wrap is desired. The range of values for the properties of PVDC copolymer films is listed in Table 5.8.

TABLE 5.8.   Typical Properties of PVDC Copolymer Films

Property	High-barrier PVDC film	High-shrink PVDC film
Specific gravity	1.68	1.62
Yield, sq in./lb/mil	16,300	16,800
Tensile strength, psi	8–16,000	8–16,000
Elongation, %	30–80	40–120
WVTR, $\frac{gm}{100 \text{ sq in.}/24 \text{ hr/mil}}$	.2	.6
O$_2$ transmission, $\frac{cc}{100 \text{ sq in.}/24 \text{ hr/atm/mil}}$	1.0	5.6
Heat sealing range	270°F–300°F	250°F–280°F
% shrink at 212°F	15–25	25–45

These films have found their major applications in food packaging, where the properties of clarity, moisture and gas barrier, and good mechanical strength are important. These include processed meats, cheese, frozen baked goods, and candy. Thin gauges, .5–1.0 mil, are sealed by heat, while heavier gauges are fabricated into bags or tubes using dielectric or electronic sealing techniques. The film can be printed by flexographic or rotogravure without surface treatment. It is also laminated to other substrates as the protective and heat seal layer for pharmaceutical packaging and as a liner for bottle caps.

Fluorocarbon Films.   The fluorocarbon films are produced from ethylene polymers where some or all of the hydrogen atoms have been replaced by fluorine atoms or fluorine and chlorine atoms. They are speciality films and generally used where the best properties of chemical resistance, thermal stability, and good barrier to moisture and gases are required. The amounts of these films that are sold is low and the price is generally high. The properties of fluorocarbon films are listed in Table 5.9.

Polytetrafluoroethylene.   Polytetrafluoroethylene (PTFE) which has the following chemical structure

TABLE 5.9. Typical Properties of Fluorocarbon Films

Property	Polytetra-fluoroethylene	Polychlorotri-fluoroethylene	Polyvinylidene Fluoride	Polyvinyl Fluoride
Specific gravity	2.15	2.08–2.13	1.75	1.4
Yield, sq in./lb/mil	12,900	13,000–13,300	15,700	20,000
Tensile strength, psi	3,000	5,000–10,000	7,000	10–19,000
Elongation, %	300	100–300	80–90	110–260
WVTR, $\frac{gm}{100 \text{ sq in.}/24 \text{ hr/mil}}$	.04–3.0	.025–.055	1.0	3.0
O_2 transmission, $\frac{cc}{100 \text{ sq in.}/24 \text{ hr/atm/mil}}$	350–700*	7–15	4	3.2
Use temperature range, °F	– 425 to + 400	– 320 to + 390	– 80 to + 300	– 100 to + 225
Sealability	Sintering Adhesive	Dielectric Impulse Hot band	Impulse Dielectric Ultrasonic	Impulse Dielectric

* Data believed taken from a sintered film which may be quite porous.

is a polyethylenic resin where all the hydrogens have been replaced by fluorine. It has superlative chemical resistance, can be used in the temperature range from − 425°F to + 400°F, has a low dielectric constant and loss factor, and a WVTR of .04 gm/100 sq in./24 hr/mil at 100°F and 95% R.H. Because of these properties it is used in electrical applications as an insulating tape and as the dielectric in capacitors. It is also used for gaskets and liners for chemical equipment. Another use is to cover hot plates, frying pans and to coat glass fiber belts due to its excellent hot release properties.

Polymonochlorotrifluoroethylene.   Polymonochlorotrifluoroethylene, having this chemical structure

also has outstanding chemical resistance, a high degree of thermal stability, and good barrier properties. Its use range is from − 320°F to 390°F with a WVTR of .025–.055 gm/100 sq in./24 hr/mil and oxygen transmission of 7–15 cc/100 sq in./24 hr/atm/mil at 73°F. The addition of the chlorine makes the polymer much more extrudable and heat formable than PTFE. Films made from this resin are clear and heat sealable by dielectric, impulse, or band heat sealers. They are used for packaging of pharmaceuticals where the completed packages must be heat sterilized and for special chemicals and hardware. Most often it is used in laminate structures.

Polyvinylidene Fluoride.   Polyvinylidene fluoride having the composition

is available in the form of a cast film and has a use temperature range from − 80°F to 300°F. It has good chemical resistance, excellent abrasion resistance, and can be sealed by impulse, dielectric, or ultrasonic techniques. Applications are for equipment liners and pump diaphragms.

Polyvinyl Fluoride.   Polyvinyl fluoride

also has good chemical resistance along with excellent outdoor weathering properties. It is used as a pigmented surfacing material for siding, wall panels, and pressure sensitive tape. It is also used as a release film for processing reinforced plastics.

Rubber Hydrochloride Films.

Rubber hydrochloride films are produced by treating rubber with hydrogen chloride. A typical structure is as follows:

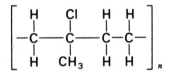

Many types of these rubber hydrochloride films are available having a range of properties for different applications. The films have excellent heat seal strength and a broad sealing range of 250°F to 350°F. Tensile strength ranges from 3,000–4,000 psi and elongation from 270% down to 12–15%. WVTR varies with type from .5–15 gm/100 sq in./24 hr/mil and oxygen transmission rate from 5–100 cc/100 sq in./24 hr/atm/mil.

The more highly plasticized films have higher elongations and transmission rates and are used in packaging fresh red meat, fresh produce, and frozen foods. Intermediate barrier films are used for baked goods and the least plasticized, highest barrier films are used for packaging cheese. Rubber hydrochloride films are also used as the heat seal ply of laminates since they also have good chemical resistance and inertness. One particular use has been as a liner in coffee bags. Dimensional stability is good and makes rubber hydrochloride usable for window carton applications.

Polyester Films.

Polyester films have great strength and good aging characteristics. A typical chemical structure is that of polyethylene terephthalate, which is the reaction product of ethylene glycol and terephthalic acid, and is as follows:

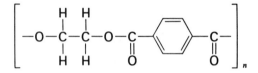

The film is biaxially oriented and has tensile strengths of 17,000 to 25,000 psi and a use temperature range from $-75°F$ to $300°F$. For many applications it is coated or laminated to obtain heat sealability. Types are available for vacuum drawing and heat shrinking.

Due to its high strength, heat stability, and clarity, polyester films are used in laminates for vacuum packaging of processed meat, cheese, boil-in-bag applications, and packaging of pharmaceuticals. As a shrink film it is used in thin gauges to wrap paper goods, toys, and hardware. It is also used in many industrial applications for its high strength and good dielectric properties. A list of properties is given in Table 5.10.

Polyamide Films.   Polyamide films are produced from two types of nylon polymer. Nylon-6 has the following chemical structure:

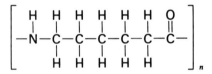

On the other hand, the structure of nylon-11 is as follows:

$$\left[\underset{\quad}{-\overset{H}{\underset{|}{N}}-(CH_2)_{10}-\overset{O}{\overset{||}{C}}-} \right]_n$$

Films from nylon-6 have higher temperature resistance and resistance to greases and oils than those made from nylon-11. Most U.S. made films are produced from nylon-6 while European films are predominantly nylon-11. Both films have good tensile strength, elongation, impact strength, and flexibility. Nylon will absorb moisture and its WVTR and gas transmission rates increase as the relative humidity increases.

Nylon will withstand autoclaving and is used for packaging pharmaceuticals that have to be sterilized. It is also used to package dough items that can be heated or baked in the package. One of the largest volume applications is as a laminate with polyethylene for deep draw vacuum packaging, where nylon's strength, grease resistance, toughness,

TABLE 5.10. Typical Properties of Polyester, Polyamide, Polyurethane and Polycarbonate Films

Property	Polyester	Polyamide Nylon 6	Polyamide Nylon 11	Polyurethane	Polycarbonate
Specific gravity	1.4	1.13	1.04	1.20–1.25	1.20
Yield, sq in./lb/mil	21,500	24,500	25,600	23,000	23,100
Tensile strength, psi	17–25,000	10–12,000	8–10,000	8–11,000	8–9,000
Elongation, %	60–120	300–500	250–400	500–800	85–105
WVTR, $\frac{gm}{100\ sq\ in./24\ hr/mil}$	1.7	.6	1.0	30–150	8
O_2 transmission, $\frac{cc}{100\ sq\ in./24\ hr/atm/mil}$	3–20	1–3	6–10	50–100	300
Use temperature, °F	–75 to 300	–100 to 200	–45 to 212	–100 to 200	–235 to 280
Sealability	Coated Types Heat seal	Dielectric or Ultrasonic	Dielectric or Ultrasonic	Heat 250–350°F	Ultrasonic or Heat 380–430°F

and flexibility are important. The laminates are usually heat sealed while dielectric or impulse sealing make better welds on the unsupported film. See Table 5.10 for a list of properties.

Polyurethane Films.   Polyurethane film and sheeting are relatively new products. Polyurethanes are a large family (related to the poly-amides) covering many types of materials having a variety of properties. The film and sheeting are produced from a resin which can be processed similarly to other thermoplastic resins.

Polyurethane films have outstanding resistance to fuels and oils, low temperature flexibility, excellent abrasion resistance, and toughness. Applications have been for packaging small parts in grease and oil, and as the outside surface of foam packs to give the units toughness. Polyurethanes have also been used as a protective coating for polyethylene packages to reduce solvent attack and permeability. Due to the film's toughness it has been used for shipping bags for chemicals, and as pouches for potable water. Other applications are being studied to find where its great toughness and barrier properties will be an advantage. See Table 5.10 for properties.

Polycarbonate Films.   The typical structure of polycarbonates is as follows:

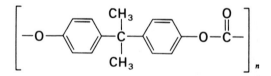

These films have excellent heat resistance, being usable in the range from $-140°F$ to $270°F$. They have excellent thermoforming properties and can be deep drawn with good detail. The mechanical properties are good and the film is chemically resistant to oils, fats, and dilute acids, but is affected by strong alkalis, aromatic hydrocarbons, and chlorinated solvents. Water vapor and gas transmission rates are relatively high.

Due to good forming characteristics, heat resistance, and toughness, polycarbonate film and sheet are used in skin and blister packaging. They are also used in laminations and for carton windows. A summary of properties is given in Table 5.10.

Polystyrene Films. Oriented polystyrene (OPS) film was first produced in Germany in the 1930's as an electrical cable insulation. It has the following structure.:

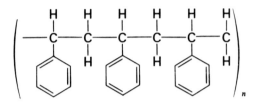

Unoriented polystyrene is a brittle, inflexible material, but biaxial orientation improves its flexibility and mechanical properties.

Oriented polystyrene films have excellent clarity, sparkle, and gloss. They show negligible water absorption, resulting in outstanding dimensional stability and aging characteristics. Tensile strength ranges from 9,000 to 10,000 psi and elongation is low. Both the WVTR and gas transmission rate of OPS film are high. The WVTR is 8 gm/100 sq in./24 hr/mil at 100°F and 90% R.H., and the O_2 transmission rate is about 300 cc/100 sq in./24 hr/atm/mil. Oriented polystyrene film is resistant to alkalis, weak acids, alcohols, oils, and greases, but is attacked or dissolved by strong acids and most organic solvents. The dielectric strength at 60 cycles is 5,000 volts/mil, which accounts for its continuing use in electrical cable insulation. Since the film is oriented, it will shrink when heated above 185°F. This, coupled with a high softening point, makes OPS films difficult to heat seal. Solvent and adhesive sealing are used in most applications. Scratch resistance, impact strength, and crease resistance are low.

With this combination of properties, the largest use for OPS film is for windows in cartons and envelopes, where the high clarity, excellent dimensional stability, and aging characteristics, together with low cost make it attractive. Another large use is in wrapping produce items like lettuce, tomatoes, cauliflower, etc. OPS sheet in gauges of 3–20 mils is used for graphic arts and in pressure formed containers. This appears to be the area of greatest potential growth because of the cost-performance ratio of this material.

WATER SOLUBLE FILMS

Many products can be packaged in water soluble films with advantage. These include household products like soaps, detergents, bleaches and dyes; food additives such as spices, flavors, yeasts and dough conditioners; and industrial and agricultural products like·sprays, chemical additives and strip packaging of seeds. Their greatest value will probably be in unit packages of premeasured amounts of product that can be used, package and all. This will save time, eliminate waste, and provide safe handling of the proper amount of product.

Three water soluble plastic films are currently produced from *polyvinyl alcohol* (PVA), *methyl cellulose* and *polyethylene oxide*. The structural formula for PVA is:

$$\left(\begin{array}{c} \text{H} \quad \text{H} \\ -\text{C}-\text{C}- \\ \text{H} \quad \text{OH} \end{array} \right)_n$$

The structure of methyl cellulose was covered in the discussion of cellulosics. The properties of these films vary with humidity conditions. The tensile strength and modulus decrease with increasing humidity, while WVTR and gas transmission rates increase as humidity increases. They can be heat sealed or solvent sealed with water and heat.

Polyvinyl alcohol films are made in thicknesses of 1–3 mils by solution casting. It is the most widely used water soluble film and is used as a release sheet for molding of reinforced plastics as well as for packaging. It has excellent gas barrier properties when dry and is used in some laminations for this property.

Methyl cellulose film is the only water soluble film which can be used in direct contact with food, and it is used for the pre-packaging of bread dough additives. Methyl cellulose is more soluble in cold water than hot water, while the solubility of PVA and polyethylene oxide films increases with increasing water temperature. Methyl cellulose powder is used as a thickener in some products and to resist the penetration of grease. Properties are listed in Table 5.11.

Miscellaneous Films.   Other speciality films are available, having exotic properties which make them suitable for particular applications. One of the newest is a *polyimide* film whose structure is as follows:

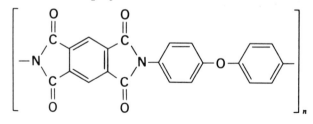

It has very high temperature stability with good mechanical and electrical properties. It has a use range of $-300°F$ to $+570°F$. Its mechanical properties are similar to those of polyester films at room temperature. Applications are in high temperature electrical uses and for hose and tubing in space vehicles.

TABLE 5.11.   Properties of Water Soluble Films

Property	Polyvinyl alcohol	Methylcellulose	Polyethylene oxide
Specific gravity	1.21	1.39	1.20
Yield, sq in./lb/mil	22,500	20,400	23,000
Tensile strength, psi	5,000–9,000	8,500–11,400	2,000–3,000
Elongation, %	300–600	10–15	900
WVTR, $\dfrac{\text{gm}}{100 \text{ sq in.}/24 \text{ hr}/\text{mil}}$	100	70	—
Oxygen transmission rate, $\dfrac{\text{cc}}{100 \text{ sq in.}/24 \text{ hr}/\text{atm}/\text{mil}}$	0–.5 (dry)	25	—
Water solubility range, °F	33–212	33–130	33–212
Heat seal range, °F	280–350	290–320	140–200

Polyacrylonitrile Films.   *Polyacrylonitrile* has the following structure:

$$\left(\begin{array}{c} \text{H} \quad \text{H} \\ | \quad\ \ | \\ -\text{C}-\text{C}- \\ | \quad\ \ | \\ \text{H} \quad \text{CN} \end{array}\right)_n$$

Its films are not commercially available at this writing, but they possess excellent gas barrier properties having an oxygen transmission rate of .03 cc/100 sq in./24 hr/atm/mil.

Phenoxy films are rigid transparent films with high impact strength. One example of the *parylene* films is poly-*p*-xylene whose structure is as follows:

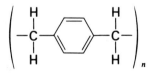

Parylene films are ductile at very low temperatures and can be used down to $-350°F$. They also possess good dielectric properties and chemical resistance.

TABLE 5.12. Prices and Properties of Plastic Films

Plastic Film Type	Price Range $/lb	Price Range ¢/1,000 sq in. @ 1 mil	High tensile strength	Toughness	Flexibility	Stiffness	Low temp. flexibility	High temp. resistance	Low MVTR	Low gas TR	Breathable	Oil and grease resistance	Chemical resistance	High dielectric strength	Good heat sealing	Good machinability	Heat formable	Outstanding Property
Cellophane	.62–.79	2.82–4.05				×									×	×	×	High speed machinability
Cellulose acetate	.67–.86	3.04–3.96		×							×						×	Clarity and sparkle
Polyacrylonitrile	1.90	8.00	×			×			×	×		×	×					.63 cc/100 sq in. O$_2$ trans. rate
Polyamide	1.75–2.15	7.20–8.75	×	×	×			×				×					×	Toughness
Polycarbonate	1.72	7.45		×		×		×										High temp. resistance
Polyethylene	.29–.36	.97–1.22		×	×		×		×				×		×		×	Low cost—many uses
Polyester	1.80–2.50	8.37–12.50	×	×		×		×										Tens. strength and abrasion resistance
Polyimide	25.00	129.90	×	×		×	×	×						×				Use range—300°F to 570°F
Polypropylene, cast	.59	1.90			×				×						×			Clarity
biaxially oriented	1.05–1.40	3.43–4.60	×	×		×			×									Abrasion resistance

Material											Remarks
oriented coated	1.40	4.85				X		X		X	X	Good mech. and barrier prop.
Polystyrene	.60	2.28			X	X	X	X	X			Dimensional stability
Polytetrafluoroethylene	11.50	89.00	X	X	X	X	X		X			Use range—425°F to 500°F
Polymonochlorotrifluoro-ethylene	6.60	50.80	X	X	X	X	X	X	X	X		Lowest MVTR (.025 gm/100 sq in.)
Polyurethane	2.00–3.00	8.70–13.00			X	X	X		X	X	X	Very tough and flexible
Polyvinylalcohol	1.38	6.14		X	X	X	X					Water soluble
Polyvinylchloride, rigid	.80–1.07	4.00–5.35	X	X		X	X	X	X	X	X	Good properties for formed parts
Polyvinylchloride, flexible	.57–.89	2.65–4.15		X	X	X		X	X	X		Stretch and shrink wraps
Polyvinylidene chloride-vinylchloride copolymer	1.08	6.60			X	X	X	X	X			Good barrier in flexible film
Polyvinylidene fluoride	8.50	53.80	X	X	X	X	X	X	X			High UV resistance, wide temp. use
Poly-p-xylene	—	—		X	X	X	X		X			Low temp. use to −350 °F
Rubber hydrochloride	1.19	4.83	X	X	X	X	X	X				Toughness and clarity

SUMMARY

Today there is a wide selection of plastic films covering a broad range of properties. Table 5.12 is a summary of film types, their price range, and outstanding properties. Each end use and application must be evaluated and a film having the proper balance of functional properties selected. When two or more films possess the necessary properties, then the selection has to be made on the basis of economics, sealability, machinability, or decorating possibilities. In considering economic factors it is necessary to evaluate the cost of the film base not only on price per pound, but also on the total performance.

For many years cellophane was the film used in largest volume, and it still continues to be widely used. This is due to its clarity, adequate barrier properties, and excellent machinability and heat sealing characteristics. However, polyethylene films have now become the volume leader. As polyethylene films became clearer and lower in price, new machines were developed to feed, fold, and seal these soft films, and users were able to take advantage of their toughness, low temperature flexibility, and moisture barrier properties. As the polypropylene and olefin copolymer films develop, the polyolefin film market will continue to grow rapidly.

The applications for PVC film and sheeting are growing every day. New formulations make a broad range of types possible, and lower prices will continue to stimulate growth. Most of the other film types are used in applications where their special properties are required, but they will probably not gain large volume acceptance due to limitations in their balance of properties, price, and performance.

For many packaging and industrial applications, no single film has the correct balance or combination of properties. In these instances laminates or structured films can be used to combine the properties of more than one type of material. These laminated and structured films are discussed at length in Chapter 6.

TABLE 5.13.   Trade Names of Films

Generic Film Type	Trade Name	Manufacturer
Regenerated cellulose	Cellophane	duPont
	Cellophane	Avisco
	Cellophane	Olin
Cellulose acetate	Kodacel	Eastman Kodak
Cellulose triacetate	Kodacel	Eastman Kodak
Cellulose acetate butyrate	Kodacel	Eastman Kodak
Cellulose acetate propionate	Forticel	Celanese

TABLE 5.13.   (continued)

Generic Film Type	Trade Name	Manufacturer
Ethyl cellulose	Ethocel sheeting	Dow
Methylcellulose	Methocel film	Dow
Polyacrylonitrile	Barex	Sohio
Polyamide	Capran	Allied Chemical
	Fosta	Foster-Grant
	Rilsan	May Industries
Polycarbonate	Lexan	General Electric
Polyester	Celnar	Celanese
	Mylar	duPont
	Kodar	Eastman Kodak
	Scotch pak	Minnesota Mining
Polyethylene	Dynafilm	Alamo Industries
	Polyfilm	Dow
	Visqueen	Ethyl Corporation
	Zendel	Union Carbide
Polyethylene, shrink film	Lexel	Dow
	Cry-O-Vac L	W. R. Grace
Polyimide	Kapton	duPont
Polypropylene	Olefane	Avisun
	Udel	Union Carbide
	Pro-fax	Hercules
	Kordite	Mobil Chemical
Polypropylene barrier coated	Clysar	duPont
	Pro-fax	Hercules
Polystyrene	Biax	Joseph Davis
	Trycite	Dow
	Polyflex	Monsanto
Polytetrafluoroethylene	Teflon	duPont
Polymonochlorotrifluoroethylene	Aclar	Allied Chemical
Polyvinyl alcohol	Reynolon	Reynolds Metal
		Monosol
Polyvinyl chloride, flexible	Resinite	Borden
	Velon	Firestone
	Vita film	Goodyear
	Reynolon	Reynolds Metal
Polyvinyl chloride, rigid	Oriex	Tenneco, Inc.
	Vynex	Tenneco, Inc.
	Mirrex	Tenneco, Inc.
	Genotherm	Kalle (Germany)
	Sumilite	Sumitomo (Japan)
Polyvinylidene chloride copolymer	Saran Wrap	Dow
	Cryovac	W. R. Grace
	Krehalon	Kureha (Japan)
Polyvinyl fluoride	Tedlar	duPont
Polyvinylidene fluoride	Kynar	Monosol
Rubber hydrochloride	Pliofilm	Goodyear

REFERENCES

De Long, R. F. and Helms, J. F., New Film Combinations, *Mod. Packaging* (November, 1965).

Eichhorn, J., Speciality Papers, Chapter XIV, Films.

Elliott, H. A. and Erb, L. F., Composite Polyolefin Films, *SPE J.* (September, 1967).

Esarove, D., Thermoplastic Polyurethanes, *Mod. Packaging* (January, 1966).

Forrester, F. J., Horner, J. T. and Sacks, Dr. W., Biaxially Oriented Polyolefin Films, *Mod. Packaging* (April, 1966).

Meyer, K. H., Natural and Synthetic High Polymers, Interscience Publishers Inc., New York.

Mounts, L. S., Saran Wrap—Low Moisture and Gas Permeability with Clarity and Strength, *Western Plastics* (July, 1956).

Perino, D. A., Polypropylene Films—Cast to Composites, *Paper, Film and Foil Converter* (March, 1967).

Ridgway, R. J., Copolymer Film Pairs Good Barrier with Low Haze Rating, *Package Engineering* (July, 1967).

Shaw, F. B., New Class of Polyolefins, *Mod. Packaging* (May, 1966)

Smith, D. W. and Trageser, D. A., Radiation-strengthened Polyethylene Films, *Mod. Packaging* (September, 1966).

Winding, C. C. and Hasche, R. L., Plastics: Theory and Practice, McGraw-Hill Book Co., Inc., New York.

Modern Packaging Encyclopedia 1966, New York, McGraw-Hill, Inc.

Polypropylenes Prospects, *Paper, Film, and Foil Converter* (January, 1966).

SIX

plastic film laminates

W. R. R. PARK

With the current proliferation of plastics and plastics films, the growing interest in and use of plastic laminates may seem somewhat surprising. However, even though such laminates are invariably more expensive than the sum of their component parts, they will generally do a particular job or achieve a balance of properties at a lower cost than is possible in any other way.

For example, consider the properties of a laminate of 1 mil cellophane combined with 1 mil of polyethylene. This combination has several properties which neither of these films possess individually in 2 mil thicknesses:

(1) Stiffness and resistance to elongation and deformation about the same as 5 mil polyethylene.

(2) Heat seal strengths of about 1,000 gm/in. which is three times that attainable with cellophane alone.

(3) Ease of printability of cellophane.

(4) Good slip characteristics of cellophane if the polyethylene layer is enclosed in the package.

(5) Better puncture resistance than cellophane.

(6) Better balanced barrier properties, since cellophane is a good gas barrier but may be moisture sensitive and polyethylene is a good moisture barrier but a relatively poor gas barrier.

The disadvantages of this combination are minimal. The clarity is not quite as good as that of cellophane, and some relatively minor slip problems may be encountered with the polyethylene layer.

The foregoing combination of properties cannot be obtained through the use of any single 2 mil film that is currently available at any price. Thus, the justification for plastic film laminates is clear, and is as follows:

(1) They provide combinations of physical properties which can be achieved in no other way.

(2) They provide combinations of properties inexpensively which heretofore could only be found in the most costly monolithic films.

Both of these are important, since users are becoming more aware of the real protective requirements needed in a wrap for their product. It is no longer sufficient for an overwrap or package just to maintain its integrity between the time the contents are packaged and when they are used. The wrapper must be sufficiently protective so that the package contents arrive at the use point in as nearly as possible their original condition, even after varying periods of shelf life.

A good example is the packaging of gumdrops. Until a few years ago, it was unusual to find really fresh and soft gumdrops packaged in transparent bags because gumdrops lost water very readily and this water in turn permeated the bag walls and was lost to the surroundings. The result was that, unless freshly packed, almost all gumdrops were hard and some were harder than others. Today gumdrops are packed in polyethylene, polyvinylidene chloride coated polyethylene, and polyethylene coated cellophane, and it is unusual to find them stale even after several months of shelf life.

This change in packaging technology has increased the initial packaging cost somewhat, but the overall costs, from the viewpoint of merchandise returned for credit, losses due to breakage, and a resistance on the part of retailers to buy goods which are packaged in an inferior way, have more than offset the packaging cost increase.

Types of Laminates. For purposes of clarity, a laminate is defined as any combination of distinctly different plastic film materials or plastic plus nonplastic materials (paper, aluminum foil, cellophane), wherein each major ply is generally thicker than $\frac{1}{4}$ mil, regardless of the method of manufacture. There is no upper limit to the possible number of plies, but two is the obvious minimum and one of these must be thermoplastic.

There are two major techniques employed in the fabrication of laminates. These are extrusion coating and adhesive lamination.

EXTRUSION COATINGS

The simpler of the two lamination techniques is extrusion coating. The range of possible products of this type alone is very large. Table 6.1

TABLE 6.1.   Extrusion Coated Papers

Substrate	Coating	Thickness (Mils)	Comments
milk carton stock	polyethylene dens. .92	.2	Milk carton board replaci wax coatings. No flak tendencies, speeds up 3,000 fpm.
20 pound pouch paper	polyethylene dens. .92	.5–2.0	For heat sealable pou having good mois barrier and strong seals.
20 pound pouch paper	polyethylene dens. .96	.5–2.0	Greater stiffness, h high temperature perties, better b than lower density ethylene.
40 pound Kraft	polypropylene dens. .90	.5 mils and up	Better grease, moistu heat resistance comparable thic of polyethylene.
40 pound Kraft	nylon, dens. 1.16	.5 mils and up	Gives exceptional ness, tear and resistance—very grease and oil ba relatively poor w rier.

describes a few of these products. To date, work has been don with polyethylene coatings, but other thermoplastics are beg find use in extrusion coating (see Figure 6.1).

Theoretically, there is no reason why any plastic which is processed by extrusion techniques cannot be coated onto other substrates. However, the extrusion technology that broadly investigated and developed only utilizes the low polyethylenes.

Extrusion coating with polyethylene has several advar adhering a prefabricated polyethylene film to paper. Firs of polyethylene are difficult to handle and to maintain fl

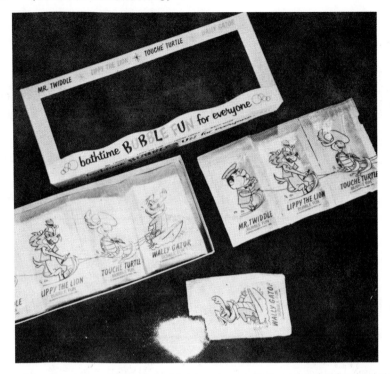

Figure 6.1.   Pouches made of paper, which have been extrusion coated with polyethylene, provide a new type of portion package for bath salts. (*Courtesy of The Dow Chemical Co.*)

them requires very low tensions, which are difficult to control at high speeds. Secondly, extrusion coating temperatures are sufficiently high, so that good mechanical bonds are obtained by resin penetration into the porous paper substrate. The same adhesion level can be obtained only by use of adhesives, when free films are laminated to paper. Thus, not only is it technically more practical to extrusion coat paper with polyethylene, but it is also considerably less expensive.

Extrusion Coating Process.   In this operation (Figure 6.2), the substrate may be coated directly, primed before coating, or corona treated before coating. Various substrates require different combinations of pretreatment to achieve desired levels of adhesion. The most important variables in this process are:

(1) Coating resin composition.
(2) Operating conditions.
(3) Substrate pretreatment.

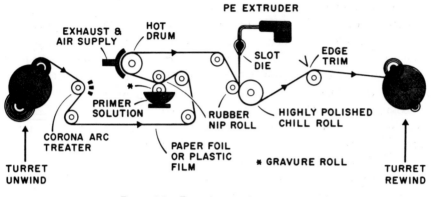

Figure 6.2. Extrusion coating process.

Coating Resins. The most generally used coating material is low density polyethylene and it is applied in thicknesses ranging from .2–3 mils. Polyethylene is extruded at 450–650°F from a slot die having an opening of at least 20 mils. Coating thicknesses are varied by changing the linear take away speeds from the die and by changing the extrusion rates. The major requirement for an extrusion coating resin is the ability to maintain film integrity during drawdown from the extruded thickness of 20 mils or so to the coating thickness of 3 mils or less. Generally, the lower molecular weight grades (higher melt index) are used for high speed coating operations. Some of these are run at speeds in excess of 2,000 fpm. The higher molecular weight resins are most often used where a thick coating is applied at relatively low speeds. The development of polyethylene extrusion coating resins to meet the multitude of requirements set for these materials is a complete branch of polymer technology by itself and is outside the scope of this text.

Operating Conditions. Several operating variables have been found to have very definite effects on the properties and quality of the finished laminate. The major items are:
(1) extrusion temperature.
(2) distance from die to coating nip.
Several things happen as extrusion temperature is increased. First, adhesion generally is improved because the polymer is air-oxidized more between the die and the nip and also because lower polymer viscosities at higher temperatures promote better surface wetting.

However, two factors will always place a practical ceiling on extrusion temperatures. First, the higher the temperature, the greater is the odor level of the finished product. Minimal odor is usually desired. Secondly, as one continues to increase the extrusion temperature, it is found that the heat sealability of the polyethylene coating progressively deteriorates. This is due to surface oxidation and it will eventually become so severe that heat sealability is completely destroyed. Thus, both odor and required heat sealability will place a practical upper limit on extrusion temperature for any given system.

Several techniques have been tried to broaden the acceptable extrusion temperature ranges. For example, if absolutely no odor can be tolerated, very low extrusion temperatures (425–500°F) must be used. Usually adhesion levels are low under these conditions, and primers or pretreatments must be used on the substrates. A section follows on this topic.

On the other hand, if very high extrusion temperatures (625°F) are required to obtain adequate adhesion, odor development can be kept to a minimum by flooding the space between die and nip with an inert gas such as nitrogen or carbon dioxide. This simply denies access of oxygen to the hot surface, thus preventing oxidation.

In other cases, one side of the hot extrudate may be flooded with oxygen and the other with nitrogen. Thus, adhesion is promoted on one side without affecting heat sealability and odor on the other side.

Three important events occur between the die and the cooling drum nip. First, the hot polymer is thinned out (drawdown) as much as 60/1. Second, the material cools. Third, a degree of surface oxidation takes place. As the die to nip distance is increased, the cooling and surface oxidation processes also proceed further. Thus, for the best adhesion, the shortest die to nip distance should be used (i.e., the highest polymer temperature at the nip) which will at the same time give an adequate oxidation level. One technique which has been used to keep the nip temperature as high as possible without using higher extrusion temperatures, is to use aluminum reflectors as shown in Figure 6.3.

The effect of drawdown* can be readily seen from the following data, where aluminum foil was coated at speeds of 175 and 350 fpm to give 1.0 and .50 mil coatings using an extrusion die temperature of 590°F.

Coating Thickness	Adhesion Strength gm/in.
1.0 mil	212
.5 mil	0

* DeHoff, G. R., and McLaughlin, Jr., T. F., *Mod. Plastics*, p. 107 (November, 1963).

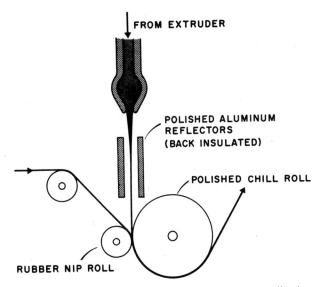

Figure 6.3.   Conserving melt temperature to improve adhesion.

The drawdown ratio was doubled to obtain the .5 mil coating. Concurrently, less surface oxidation could occur, since residence time between the die and the nip was halved. The polyethylene was only half as thick at the nip. Thus, it would have cooled further than the 1.0 mil film and the interface nip temperature would be lower than it would be with the 1.0 mil coating. This combination of effects drops the adhesion level from a useful to a nonpractical level.

Operating conditions can have very marked effects on the finished laminate, and considerable work is usually required to establish an optimum compromise of operating conditions for each particular coating job.

Substrate Pretreatments.   The development of adhesion between polyethylene and various substrates is an aspect of extrusion coating which has received a great deal of attention. When a porous substrate like paper is coated, adhesion is developed by a mechanical interpenetration of polymer into the paper fibers. In this case no pretreatment is required to obtain a satisfactory level of adhesion under common extrusion coating conditions.

With nonporous substrates like aluminum foil or cellophane, some type of surface pretreatment may be required to obtain an adequate level of adhesion of the extruded polyethylene. Surface treatment is indicated, even for paper, when coating speeds are sufficiently high that a strong interpenetration type bond can no longer be obtained.

Three approaches to adhesion enhancement have so far been developed. These are:

(1) Surface modification of substrate by mechanical means.
(2) Use of an adhesion promoting primer coating on substrate.
(3) A combination of (1) and (2).

Mechanical Surface Treatments. Two mechanical surface treatment techniques are commonly used. These are flame treatment and corona-arc discharge. Both appear to function through an oxidation of the film, which introduces polar groups into the surface. This has the effect of rendering the substrate surface more compatible with a freshly oxidized polyethylene surface, which in turn promotes adhesion between the two.

Flame treatment (Figure 6.4) is not widely used for surface modification, since it appears to have no advantages over corona-arc discharge treatment and has not nearly the flexibility or ease of control. A typical corona-arc treater is illustrated in Figure 6.5. This unit is usually mounted in line with the extrusion coating head. It is a simple unit to operate and requires a minimum of maintenance. The degree of treatment is regulated by rheostat adjustment of the power fed to the discharge electrode. This treatment has been used to promote adhesion of polyethylene to all of the materials shown in Table 6.2.

With all of these materials there was a demonstrable improvement in adhesion. However, other substrates do not necessarily react in this manner, and each new material must be evaluated to see if corona

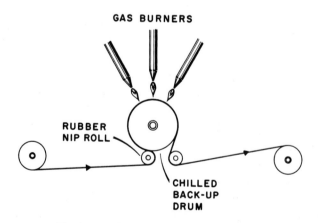

Figure 6.4.   Flame treatment of plastic film.

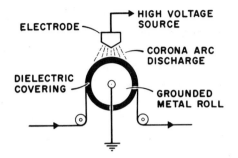

Figure 6.5.   Corona arc discharge treatment of plastic films.

TABLE 6.2.   Effect of Corona Treatment of Substrate on Adhesion†

(1.0 mil coating of polyethylene applied at 250 fpm)

Film	Adhesion gm/in. Without Corona		Adhesion gm/in. With Corona	
	Fresh	*Aged*	*Fresh*	*Aged*
Polypropylene	0*	—	>900	—
Polystyrene, 10 mils	0**	—	600–800	—
MSBO Cellophane coated on wettable side	0***	59 3 days	10	105 3 days
MSBO Cellophane Polyvinylidene chlorine coated cellophane coated on uncoated side	40–100**	—	300–500	—
	>150*	<40	105	225
Wet strength paper—.5 mil coating	29%		100%	

† Noll, P. B., and McAllister, J. E., Paper, Film and Foil Converter, p. 46 (October, 1963).
*USI's Petrothene 205-15, dens. .928, M.I. 3, or 212-2, dens. .915, M.I. 12.
** Petrothene 203-2 (no slip additive).
*** Petrothene 203-49 (contains slip additive).

treatment will have advantages. Likewise, the polyethylene coating formulation can have an effect on the adhesion level that is obtained. Generally, those compositions containing migratory slip agents will not respond as well to corona treatment. Apparently the slip agent can migrate to the polyethylene-substrate interface and cause a diminution in adhesion.

Primer Treatments for Substrate.   A number of materials have been found to be effective in promoting polyethylene adhesion to a variety of substrates. These materials are generally applied to the substrate in very thin coats. Best results seem to be obtained when the thinnest practical continuous coating is applied. Optimum primer coating weight is usually of the order of a few milligrams per square foot.

These primers seem to function by being of such a chemical nature that the oxidized, extruded polyethylene surface will adhere strongly to them, and the primer in turn will adhere strongly to the substrate. Since these materials have low cohesive strength, too thick a prime coat will actually lead to a loss of adhesion. Thus, optimum concentrations must be found for particular primers, substrates, and type of extrusion coating.

The general chemical types of primers that have so far found commercial utility* are:

(1) Polyalkyleneimine (Polyethyleneimine–PEI).
(2) Organic titanates.
(3) Polyurethanes.
(4) Polyesters.
(5) Colloidal silica.

It is probable that other chemical types can function effectively, and further development work is expected in this area. Also, not all of these types function equally well with all substrates, so that the selection of a primer for a given system still requires quite extensive screening. Examples of the type of results to be expected with different primers are found in Table 6.3.

TABLE 6.3.†   Adhesion Strength Data—Polyethylene on Mylar

Primer	Extrusion Coating thickness (mils)	Adhesion strength (gm/in.)	
		Fresh	After 10 days
None	1.0	0	0
	.5	0	0
Polyethyleneimine*	1.0	568	844
	.5	283	468
Polydibutyl titanate**	1.0	289	504
	.5	153	325
Colloidal silica***	1.0	372	0
	.5	459	68

† DeHoff, G. R., and McLaughlin, Jr., T. F., *Mod. Plastics*, p. 107 (November, 1963).
* Borden SO-242.
** Dupont Tyzor PB.
*** Dupont Ludox.

These data illustrate again the effect of coating thickness on adhesion. An effective primer works better with a thick coating, because the coating maintains a higher combining temperature at the cooling roll

* Major primer suppliers are duPont, American Cyanamid, Borden, National Starch, Adcote.

nip. Also, aging may improve or degrade the bond strength of a primer. Aging tests constitute an important part of new primer evaluations. Particular primer types are not always as effective with different substrates. Table 6.4 shows the effect of using the same primers, coating weights, and coating conditions on a different substrate.

TABLE 6.4.   Adhesion Strength Data—Polyethylene on Aluminum Foil

Primer	Extrusion coating thickness (mils)	Adhesion strength (gm/in.)	
		Fresh	After 10 Days
None	1.0	212	459
	.5	0	45
Polyethyleneimine	1.0	313	295
	.5	268	281
Polydibutyl titanate	1.0	450	699
	.5	256	404
Colloidal silica	1.0	535	547
	.5	262	243

In this case, primers appeared particularly effective in promoting adhesion of thin coatings (low combining temperatures) but only showed marginal improvements in the adhesion of thicker coatings (i.e., 1 mil coating adhered well to untreated aluminum foil).

The effectiveness of polyethyleneimine primers can be improved on certain substrates by formulating these primers with oxidizing agents. These agents in turn cause polyethylene to adhere at lower temperatures or higher rates or both, apparently by interface oxidation which enables materials to be better bonded by the imine primer. Table 6.5

TABLE 6.5.†   Extrusion Coating of Primed Regenerated Cellulose*

Extrusion Temp. (°C)	.5% PEI Adhesion (gm/in.)	.5% PEI + .3% CrO_3 Adhesion (gm/in.)	Heat seal (gm/in.)
260	125	760	—
270	125	1,000	5,600
280	250	1,000	5,900
290	630	1,000	4,100
300	890	1,000	2,500
320	890	1,000	3,000

† British Patent 928,257 (June 12, 1963).
* Coating thickness 1.0 mil.

shows the effect of an oxidizing agent plus polyethyleneimine on the adhesion of polyethylene to regenerated cellulose. Note that the heat seal strength drops off as extrusion temperature is increased. Thus, not only does the oxidizing agent cause better adhesion at lower extrusion temperatures, but it may attain a stronger heat seal than can otherwise be obtained under any conditions, because polyethylene is strongly adhered at low temperature, without being appreciably oxidized on the heat sealing side.

In summary, then, primers offer a means of obtaining adequate polyethylene adhesion to many substrates at lower melt temperature and higher speeds than can be attained without them. It appears that primers will play an increasingly important role in extrusion coating, where the trend is towards higher speed operations.

Extrusion Lamination.   Extrusion lamination is a specialized use of extrusion coating, where a hot extruded film of polyethylene is trapped between two other webs and cooled, as shown in Figure 6.6.

As in the case with extrusion coating, this process is applicable to any thermoplastic material, but the technology has been highly developed only for polyethylene. The same adhesion problems are present, and substrates may have to be treated in the ways mentioned earlier to achieve adequate adhesion levels.

The most common 3 ply laminates made this way are cellophane, PE–cellophane, paper–PE–paper, polyester–PE–foil, cellophane–PE–foil, foil–PE–paper. Figure 6.7 shows foil and paper being combined with an extrusion of polyethylene. It is probably possible to develop techniques for combining any two film materials using polyethylene as an adhesive in an extrusion lamination operation.

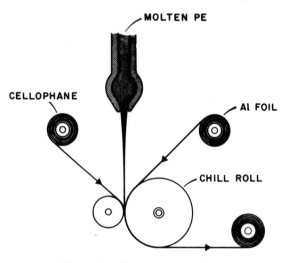

Figure 6.6.   Extrusion lamination.

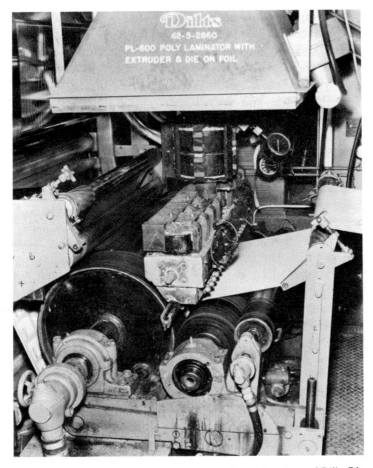

Figure 6.7. A typical extrusion lamination operation. (*Courtesy of Dilts Div., Black Clawson Co.*)

ADHESIVE LAMINATIONS

This process consists of applying an adhesive to one ply, then combining it with another before drying (wet bonding), or drying the adhesive and bonding the second ply with heat or pressure or both (dry bonding).

Wet bonding is limited to laminates wherein one ply is very porous (paper), since solvent must be able to pass through a ply as the adhesive is being dried. Thus, this process is used only with paper and foil, or paper and film. Usually aqueous adhesives such as casein, sodium silicate, starch, polyvinyl acetate latex, rubber latex, and dextrin are employed.

Dry bonding is considerably more versatile in that any two materials can be laminated once an adhesive system has been developed. Either water based or solvent based adhesives are used. Both are applied, then dried and cured, if necessary, by the application of heat. Common lacquer type adhesives are such materials as epoxies, polyurethanes, urea-formaldehydes, and polyamides. These types generally require chemical curing before developing their best properties. Others, which do not require curing, are vinyl acetate, vinyl chloride, rubber, nitro-cellulose, and polyesters. Dried thicknesses of these adhesives are usually well under 1 mil and may be as low as .05 mil. Generally, how-ever, adhesives lose their effectiveness at very low thicknesses largely because they are not able to completely wet the surface to be bonded.

When the adhesive is adequately dried or cured, the coated ply is combined with an uncoated ply through the application of heat and/or pressure in a nip. The types of materials most often laminated in this manner are typified by polyester–foil, acetate–foil, pliofilm-foil, cello-phane–foil, vinyl–foil, nylon–polyethylene and cellophane–polyethy-lene. Any such combinations may subsequently be extrusion coated or even adhesive laminated with other webs to continue to build a specific desired degree of protection into a laminate. Generally, four or at most five layers are sufficient, but any number can theoretically be combined.

SPECIALIZED LAMINATING TECHNIQUES

A new laminating technique was developed in 1963 by Kordite Corporation. They produce a plastic film, "triKor", having a total thickness of 1 mil, and composed of a three layer sandwich consisting of two outer plies of medium density polyethylene and a core of polypropylene (see Figures 6.8 and 6.9). The manufacturing technique is not extrusion lamination or adhesive lamination but a novel approach which can best be described as simultaneous extrusion through a single die.

This film was specifically designed to fill the needs of the bread wrap market, and it does this very well. It has all the advantages of polyethy-

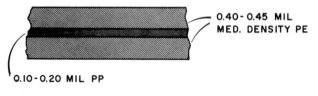

0.40- 0.45 MIL
MED. DENSITY PE

0.10-0.20 MIL PP

Figure 6.8.   Kordite's triKor.

Figure 6.9. TriKor film. New 3-ply lamination film will wrap a variety of bread loaves. Polypropylene core permits a wide selection of end labels and inner bands because of greater heat resistance at "label sealing" temperatures. Film's polyethylene outer plies assure good cold temperature strength, preventing brittleness and splitting during winter season. (*Courtesy of Kordite Corp., Films Div.*)

lene combined with the ability to heat seal over a broader temperature range (75–100° range as opposed to 5–15° range for pure polyethylene or polypropylene). It also has good low temperature flexibility (which cast polypropylene lacks), since it is composed largely of polyethylene. Because the layers do not adhere strongly to one another, the heat seals are relatively easy to peel open but have more than adequate strength to remain sealed during normal handling.

Other examples of this type of laminate will almost certainly appear. Their utility may be limited, however, unless ways are found to improve interlayer adhesion. Poor adhesion results in weak heat seals and in most overwrap applications the stronger the seal, the more valuable and practical is the film.

Hot Combining.   Another film development, which is similar in philosophy to that behind the evolution of triKor, is Dow Chemical's "Saranpac." This laminate and the associated process equipment were developed jointly by the Dow Chemical Co. and the Oscar Mayer Co. specifically for meat overwrapping. "Saranpac" provides the best meat wrapping system available today. The product is made by combining three different plastic plies directly after they have been extruded from slot dies, as shown in Figure 6.10.

The three plies, "Saran" 18 (outer), PVC88 (center), and "Saran" 22 (inner) each serve a specific function and have been tailormade for these

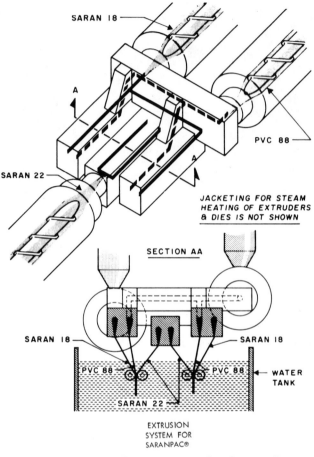

SARAN 18

A

PVC 88

SARAN 22

JACKETING FOR STEAM
HEATING OF EXTRUDERS
& DIES IS NOT SHOWN

SECTION AA

SARAN 18

SARAN 18

PVC 88

PVC 88

WATER
TANK

SARAN 22

EXTRUSION
SYSTEM FOR
SARANPAC®

Figure 6.10.   Extrusion system for "Saranpac"®.

functions. The "Saran" 22 is a crystallizable formulation having a relatively long induction period before it crystallizes, particularly at low temperature. This layer remains almost entirely amorphous until the package has been completely fabricated. While it is in this supercooled amorphous condition, it is capable of giving a hermetic seal with another layer of "Saran" 22 when the layers are simply pressed together.

Since "Saran" 22 is the inner layer on both lid and formed package, this feature is utilized to make the meat package air tight. While it adheres strongly to itself when amorphous, it does not stick to other materials to any appreciable extent.

The PVC 88 is used as a component because it adds low temperature toughness, which saran alone does not have. Also, since it is less expensive than saran, greater thicknesses can economically be used to give a desired degree of stiffness.

"Saran" 18, the outer layer material, is made from a rapidly crystallizing formulation with a higher vinylidene chloride content than "Saran" 22, and it therefore has better barrier properties. It also contributes slip properties, since it rapidly crystallizes and changes from tacky and amorphous to crystalline and slick.

"Saranpac," the laminate, must also have some overall properties to be successful. In this application, as seen in Figure 6.10, two webs of "Saranpac" are produced simultaneously. One becomes the bottom and the other the top of the meat container. These webs are combined as shown in Figure 6.11. Figures 6.12 and 6.13 show other aspects. In order to do this successfully, the composite film must be drawn into both the top and bottom of the mold without wrinkling. Secondly, when vacuum is applied, the film must give a contour wrap around the package contents, again without wrinkling. Thus, the laminate performance is just as critical as the performance of each of its components. The completed package is then heat treated with radiant energy to complete the crystallization of both inner and outer saran plies, particularly the Saran 22 layer.

The whole "Saranpac" concept is based on two facets of saran technology:

(1) Amorphous saran seals strongly to itself at low temperature.

(2) It is possible to supercool saran and hold it for relatively long periods at a very low crystalline content level.

In this latter regard, saran differs from many other crystallizable polymers, and Figure 6.14 demonstrates this behavior difference graphically.

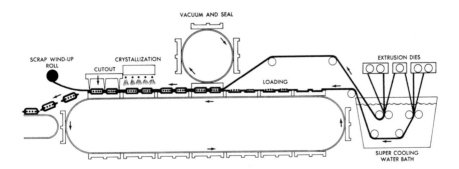

Figure 6.11.   "Saranpac"® process.

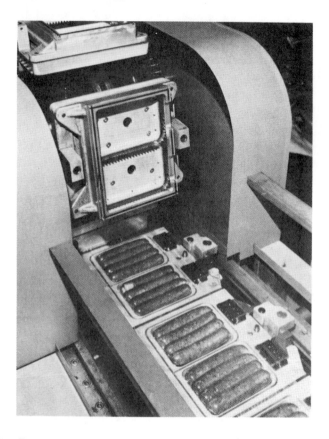

Figure 6.12.   Twin packages entering cutout station on "Saranpac"® line. Devices to draw vacuum are visible at lower right.

"Saranpac" has allowed the practical shelf life of several meat products to be extended to six weeks or more. This is at least a five fold improvement that is possible because vacuum packing eliminates the growth of mold-causing aerobic bacteria. Also, meat does not change color, for it is protected against oxygen, initially by the vacuum and in the long term by the gas barrier properties of the laminate. Other advantages of the "Saranpac" concept include reduced leaker losses and more economical inventory warehousing and production situations than are possible with more conventional packages.

Laminate Applications.   It would be nearly as difficult to itemize all the possible uses for laminates as it would be to describe all possible

Figure 6.13.   A typical completed "Saranpac"® package.

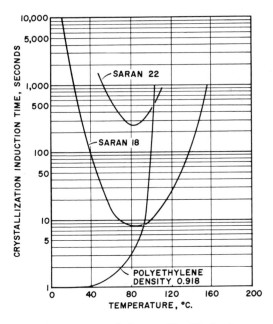

Figure 6.14.   The upper curve is typical of saran-22, while the lower curve is similar to that of saran-18. The lower curve shows that if the extruded hot melt is reduced below 100°C in less than 6 sec, it can be held amorphous for increasingly longer times as the temperature is lowered.

TABLE 6.6. Typical Laminates

Materials	Characteristics	Typical Uses
Polycarbonate-e*-PE 1 2**	Tough, transparent, puncture resistant.	Skin packaging for rough use.
Cellophane-e-PE .8–2 .5–2	Tough, heat sealable.	Saran coated versions used for vacuum and gas packing, i.e., nuts.
Acetate-a-Pliofilm .3–1.5 .5–1.5	Flexible, scratch resistant, clear.	Pill pouches.
Cellophane-a-Pliofilm 2 .5–1.5	Greaseproof, toughness.	Tailored for N_2 nut packaging.
Foil-a-Paper-e-PE .3–.5 1–2	Good moisture barrier, fin type or back seal pouches.	Soup mixes, drink powders, dry milk solids.
Cellophane-Cellophane*** .8–2.0 .8–2.0 (heat sealed together)	Locked in printing, good durability, good machinability.	Heavy duty bags and overwraps, frozen food.
Paper-a-acetate .5–2.0	Glossy, scratch resistant.	Record covers, paper back books.
Cello-e-PE-a-Saran .8–2.0 1–3 .5–2.0	Excellent flexible transparent tough barrier.	Pharmaceuticals.

Construction (mils thickness)	Properties	Uses
Acetate-a-foil-c-vinyl .8-2 .25- .1-.5 1	Excellent barrier, opaque, heat sealing.	Pouch packaging of light and oxygen sensitive materials such as drink powders and pharmaceuticals.
Cellophane-e-PE-e-foil-a-PE .8-2 .5- .3-1 1-3 1.5	Excellent gas, moisture barrier, trapped printing.	Single use pouches—ketchup, mustard, jam, etc., freeze dried foods.
Paper-e-PE-foil-e-PE .5-1.5 .3-1 1-3	Rugged strong heat seals and good barrier.	Dehydrated soups, military packaging in heavy plies.
Paper-e-PE-e-foil-c-vinyl .5-1.5 .3-1 .1-.5	Readily heat sealed, good barrier.	Instant coffee powder.
Cellophane-e-PE-e-Paper-a-foil-PE 1-2 .5 .3 1.5	Good machinability, excellent opaque barrier, tough heavy duty, glossy, and scratch resistant.	Gas packing of racked merchandise such as dehydrated spaghetti sauce.
Paper-e-PE .2-5.0	Barrier, heat sealable and printable.	Pouches for hardware fittings, milk bottles.
Polyester***-a-PE .5-2.0 e .5-3.0	Gas and moistureproof seal, tough, stable at 100°C.	Boil in a pouch construction, formable meat tray packs, cheesewrap.
Paper-e-PE-c-saran .2-1.0 .2	Very good gas barrier, heat sealable, printable.	Pouches for moist items, dried milk or dehydrated soups, etc.

* a-Adhesive lamination, e-extrusion coating, c-lacquer coating.
** Numbers under components represent mils thickness.
*** May be plain or coated.

laminates. However, a generic sample of a number of these should serve to demonstrate their utility (see Table 6.6). Figures 6.15 and 6.16 show other aspects.

Generally, each ply in a laminate is added to contribute one or more specific properties to the whole. The thickness of each ply is decided by balancing cost versus performance as it is related to thickness. One hopes to arrive at the thinnest, least expensive laminate that will have adequate properties to consistently meet the specifications of the application.

Thus, it follows that the more expensive film materials, such as polymonochlorotrifluoroethylene, polytetrafluoroethylene, and poly-carbonates, are not likely to find widespread use in laminates, since it

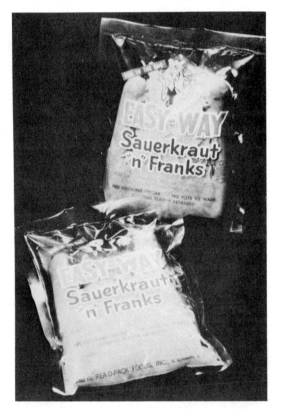

Figure 6.15.   Boil-in-a-bag is a marketing concept which has many exponents. Part of the concept's success can be attributed to an improved film lamination from which the package is made; a lamination of polyester film and medium density polyethylene. In this example the three-color design of the pouches is reverse-printed on the polyester outer lamination, protecting the printing from handling abrasion and eliminating any possible contact between printing ink and cooking water.

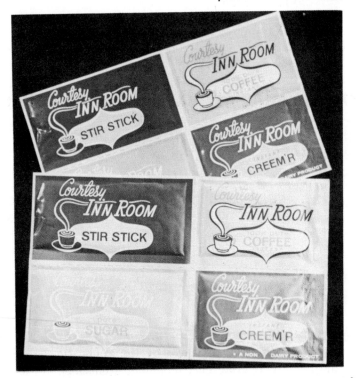

Figure 6.16.   A moderately complex laminate of paper, polyethylene, aluminum foil, and a double coating of heat sealing vinyl is used for this multipurpose pouch pack.

will usually be less expensive to use a double or triple thickness of some less expensive polymer to obtain the desired degree of a particular property.

The Future for Film Laminates.   It seems likely that the trend to more complex laminates will continue. This trend probably will be accompanied by much closer scrutiny of cost-performance-thickness data as more "in use" information is collected. Laminating speeds will have to become higher, and more attention will be paid to primer and adhesive systems which may perform better at lower cost and higher speeds. No spectacular improvements are anticipated in heat seal strengths, since these are already nearly at the theoretical maximum.

Packaging trends appear to be progressing toward more tailor-making of materials through the extensions of technology to suit existing large markets. Both Kordite's "triKor" and Dow's "Saranpac" laminates are prime examples of this approach to new laminating principles. Other developments of this general type can probably be expected.

SEVEN

thermoforming of plastic film and sheet

W. R. R. PARK

Introduction. Thermoforming is the conversion of plastic film or sheet into shaped, functional articles by the application of heat and pressure in the presence or absence of a mold. Items like plastic cottage cheese tubs and lids, cookie trays, meat and produce trays, blister packages, and so on are produced by this technique.

Use of the technique did not become widespread until around 1950, when for the first time, highly automated equipment became generally available. Prior to this time, thermoforming had been an art, and an expensive art, since each user had to develop and fabricate his own machinery for the job. With the breakthrough in mechanical know-how came much improved economics. Plastic articles could now compete costwise with paper in some applications.

As experience in thermoforming grew, it became evident that many things could be done with plastic film and sheet which could never have been done with paper or cardboard. Two examples are skin packaging and blister packaging. In the former, the item to be packaged is mounted on a cardboard backing, and heated film is drawn by vacuum around the part so that it acts as its own mold. On the other hand, blister packaging utilizes a preformed blister which need not have the exact shape of the article to be packed. A trip through any hardware store will show many examples of both of these packaging concepts. Hinges with their mounting screws may be skin packaged together.

Tubes of special cements are often blister packed. This type of packaging has been one of the prime factors in converting hardware stores more towards the less expensive, self-service type of retail establishment.

Thus, plastic thermoforming came into its own as another method for fabricating plastic into useful and decorative articles. The technique filled a gap in the spectrum of plastics processing methods, since it is not only difficult but also expensive and slow to fabricate any type of thin walled plastic container by injection molding. Injection molds seldom have more than four cavities, while thermoforming techniques allow the simultaneous fabrication of twenty, fifty, even hundreds of identical items simultaneously dependent on the part size and on the dimensions of the forming machines.

A natural evolution of this trend has been toward the development of equipment which will form, fill, and seal in one automated line. Individual jelly containers are fabricated in this manner. PVC sheet is fed in one end of the unit, multiple cavities are formed and indexed under a filling head, then the material proceeds to a sealing station where a heat sealable coated foil is sealed across the top. The completed units are die-cut at the next station and may even be automatically packaged at the final station. Some pills are now being individually packed and sealed in single blisters. Unit containers of salt and pepper can also be made this way. See also "Saranpac", p. 161.

Vacuum Forming. Figure 7.1 illustrates a relatively simple automated vacuum forming cycle. This cycle can be as low as 2–3 seconds for thinner films which are not stretched very far or over twenty seconds for thicker sheets which must undergo a greater stretch ratio. The most common thicknesses of film or sheet used in vacuum forming will fall between 4–20 mils.

Many variations on this basic forming theme are used. Each modification has as its aim the improvement in properties of the finished part. When, for example, a deep container of small diameter is to be made, it is found that the bottom edges and walls will become very thin in the simple drawing operation shown in Figure 7.1. This uneven material thickness distribution can be much improved through the use of a "plug-assist" as shown in Figure 7.2.

This plug carries a section of the sheet close to the bottom of the mold without drawing it thinner. The application of vacuum in the mold then completes the cycle, and if the plug has been well designed, a part having relatively uniform wall thickness will be obtained. While many detailed differences are possible in vacuum forming, regular and plug assist operations constitute the majority of applications.

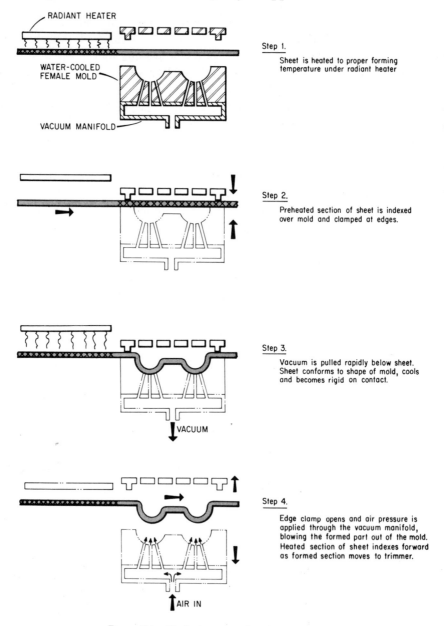

RADIANT HEATER

Step 1.
Sheet is heated to proper forming temperature under radiant heater

WATER-COOLED FEMALE MOLD

VACUUM MANIFOLD

Step 2.
Preheated section of sheet is indexed over mold and clamped at edges.

Step 3.
Vacuum is pulled rapidly below sheet. Sheet conforms to shape of mold, cools and becomes rigid on contact.

VACUUM

Step 4.
Edge clamp opens and air pressure is applied through the vacuum manifold, blowing the formed part out of the mold. Heated section of sheet indexes forward as formed section moves to trimmer.

AIR IN

Figure 7.1.   Typical vacuum forming cycle.

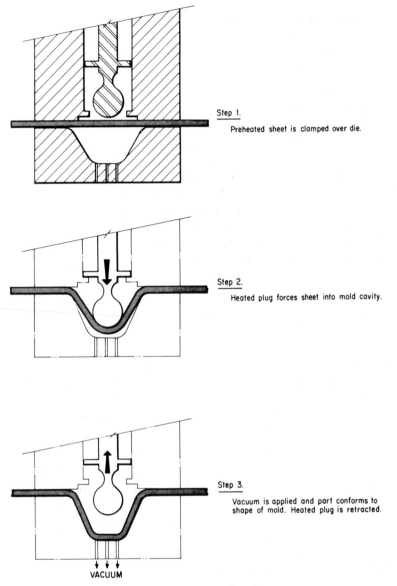

Step 1.

Preheated sheet is clamped over die.

Step 2.

Heated plug forces sheet into mold cavity.

Step 3.

Vacuum is applied and part conforms to shape of mold. Heated plug is retracted.

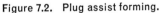

VACUUM

Figure 7.2. Plug assist forming.

At the completion of the forming cycle, the part is cut from the web in two possible ways. It may be trimmed while still in the mold, or it may be indexed to a trimming station separate from the forming area. In the former case, trimming may be either by shear cutting or by a steel rule die. Shear cutting appears to be favored for a separate station.

Pressure Forming.   Pressure forming is a logical extension of vacuum forming. The latter has a maximum forming pressure of 15 psi, while the former can have unlimited forming pressures, although 50–150 psi is most common. Pressure forming is used to obtain greater detail in the formed part and to form materials which require greater than atmospheric forming pressure. An example of such a material is biaxially oriented polystyrene sheet.

This material, when raised to a forming temperature, exhibits strong retractile forces (orientation stress release), which may prevent perfect mold contouring under low pressures. However, oriented polystyrene has an excellent balance between its physical properties and its price. Thus it is worthwhile to build special machinery to handle it through the application of a higher level of forming pressure. In matter of fact, the first pressure forming machines were built especially to handle oriented polystyrene sheet. A typical forming sequence is shown in Figure 7.3. Again, it is possible to trim either in the mold or at a separate trimming station. The most modern pressure formers have even been adapted to plug-assist operations. Figure 7.4 shows a typical commercial unit.

Forming Conditions.   The establishment of forming conditions for a given material, a given mold, etc., has always been a trial and error process. Usually, one is interested in using the lowest possible heating time at the lowest platen temperature. This combination can be established quite rapidly by determining the Forming Area Diagram for the particular equipment and film in question. Figure 7.5 is such a diagram. Ideal conditions would be one second heat time at 290°F. Higher temperatures cause the sheet to adhere to the platen, and lower temperatures require longer heating times to obtain satisfactory parts. An optimum mold contact time must also be determined, since the formed sheet must cool to below its shrink temperature before being removed from the mold or else it will distort. Typical cooling times range from a fraction to a few seconds.

Blister Packaging.   Blister packs provide a major outlet for thermoformable sheet. They can be made by either vacuum or pressure forming techniques, and they utilize all types of plastic sheet. The package is generally completed by glueing or stapling the flanges of the blister to a backing board, after having inserted the item into the blister. The backing board has all the graphics on it, while the blister is

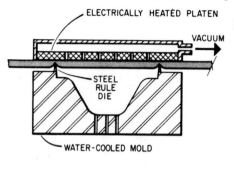

Step 1.

Sheet is indexed forward and held against heating platen with vacuum. Steel rule die (which circumscribes mold) cuts one fourth through sheet to hold and prevent shrinkback.

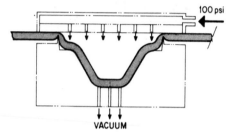

Step 2.

After a one-to-two second heat cycle, air pressure is applied through the platen while vacuum is applied through the mold.

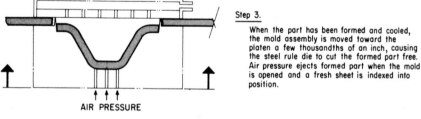

Step 3.

When the part has been formed and cooled, the mold assembly is moved toward the platen a few thousandths of an inch, causing the steel rule die to cut the formed part free. Air pressure ejects formed part when the mold is opened and a fresh sheet is indexed into position.

Figure 7.3.   Typical pressure forming operation.

generally clear. This packaging technique provides a near perfect marriage of plastic sheet and cardboard. The packaged item is perfectly visible and readily displayed. Often the blister will be made to contour the item to be packed in order to minimize its movement. A few of the more common conformations are illustrated in Figure 7.6.

Skin Packaging. This is a special type of blister packaging, where the item to be packed actually serves as the mold for its own plastic cover. It is one of the least expensive newer packaging methods and

Figure 7.4.   A typical pressure forming unit. (*Courtesy of Brown Machine Co.*)

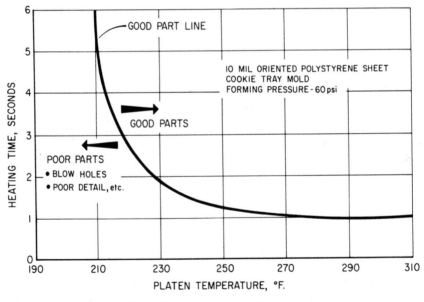

Figure 7.5.   Forming area diagram.

lends itself to the immobilization of multiple small parts without interfering with their visibility. The finished package tends to discourage pilfering since the backing board is usually of an awkward size for pocketing. Skin packaging is generally done as shown in Figure 7.7.

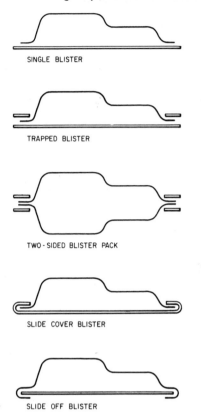

SINGLE BLISTER

TRAPPED BLISTER

TWO-SIDED BLISTER PACK

SLIDE COVER BLISTER

SLIDE OFF BLISTER

Figure 7.6. Typical blister types.

Many modifications have been worked out, for this method often is the least expensive packaging technique possible. For small items, thin films (2–5 mils) of polyethylene, PVC, or ionomer will work very well.

Table 7.1 lists the common plastic film and sheet used in thermoforming.

Future Developments. As the markets expand for thermoformed plastic items, a number of logical developments can be foreseen. Prime among these will be the "complete forming line", where plastic granules are fed in one end and printed containers are automatically boxed or filled at the other end. In this type of operation, which will be really practical only for the largest volume items of one size and color, sheet will be extruded hot, conveyed to the forming station without cooling, formed, trimmed, (trim scrap will be immediately ground and recycled with the virgin pellets into the extruder hopper), printed, stacked, and boxed without being touched by human hand.

TABLE 7.1.   Common Thermoforming Plastics

Type	Thickness mils	Sq In./Lb/ 10 mils	$/Lb approx.	Vacuum Forming	Pressure Forming	Blister	Skin	Comments
Cellulose acetate, butyrate, proprionate	5–20	2,200	.85	Yes	Yes	Yes	—	Tough parts with high sparkle.
Oriented polystyrene	3–20	2,600	.40	No	Yes	Yes	No	Most rigid material in thin clear sections at lowest cost/unit.
Rubber modified polystyrene	10–40	2,600	.50	Yes	Yes	—	—	Hazy in non-pigmented form, gives excellent detail.
Rigid vinyl	5–20	2,000	.60	Yes	Yes	Yes	No	Good detail, good barrier and toughness.
Flexible vinyl	3–10	2,000	.60	Yes	Yes	No	Yes	Requires careful heat control. Gives tough flexible parts.
Polyethylene (low density)	3–30	3,000	.40	Yes	Yes	No	Yes	Most applications in thin skin packs.
Polyethylene (med. and high density)	10–30	2,900	.50	Yes	Yes	Yes	Yes	Much more rigid than low density PE.
Polycarbonate	10–60	2,300	1.50	Yes	Yes	Yes	Yes	Excellent for deep draws and toughness.
Nylon-6	2–30	2,450	2.00	Yes	Yes	Yes	Yes	Even thin gauges can be deep drawn. Superb for resistance to tearing, splitting, and pinholing.
Fluorohalocarbon	2–20	1,300	5.00	Yes	Yes	Yes	Yes	Excellent barrier, chemical resistance and high temperature resistance.

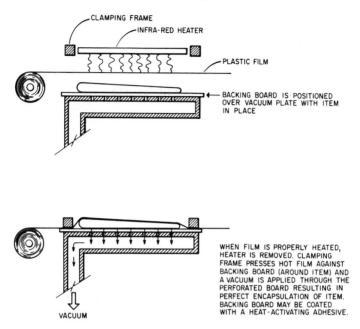

Figure 7.7.   Skin packaging.

It seems possible that sheet metal drawing techniques will also find utility in forming of plastic sheet. Cold drawing and punching have not so far been extensively utilized but appear to have potential for simple parts using some plastics.

EIGHT

growth areas for plastic films

W. R. R. PARK

While packaging and general overwrap markets still consume the major part of the output of plastic films, it may not be in this area that plastic films will experience their greatest growth in the future. Many packaging applications are essentially saturated with plastic films, and growth in these markets will increase about as fast as the Gross National Product. A good example is the overwrapping of tobacco products. This market for plastic films is dominated by nitrocellulose coated cellophanes. While this may not always be so (coated oriented polypropylene films may become strong contenders), the size of this outlet for films will not increase rapidly, since all such products are already overwrapped. This, by the way, is not yet true in Europe, where many cigarettes are packaged without benefit of a cellophane protective covering.

Thus, it is to new packaging concepts and new nonpackaging uses that we must look for the greatest volume growth in the plastics films business. The number of such developments in the last few years is quite startling. It seems to indicate that a trend is developing which emphasizes fuller exploitation of the unique physical properties of many different films. For example, polytetrafluoroethylene film ("Teflon") is much too expensive to compete in the general overwrap market. However, it has three outstanding properties. It can withstand prolonged exposure to temperatures in excess of 450°F; it has a very low coefficient of friction, and very few things will stick to it. In view of

its cost of over $5.00/lb in thin gauges, it seems unlikely that any uses would be found for this material. However, its extremely low coefficient of friction and its antisticking property has led to extensive use in such areas as heat seal bar covers. Before "Teflon" film became available the heat seal bars on overwrap machines handling coated cellophane had to be cleaned frequently to remove tacky deposits which accumu lated. A layer of "Teflon" tape on the seal bar makes this part of tl unit almost maintenance free and easily pays for itself many times ov in increased operating efficiency.

These types of applications, which take advantage of the outstand physical characteristics of plastic film, are increasing in number. W such applications develop within the field of packaging, usually s new concept is involved. Examples are shrink wraps and water sol films. Both will be discussed at length later. Of perhaps more int because of larger potential markets are the new nonpackaging use plastic films. Examples are the uses of plastic films in architectur agriculture, synthetic fabrics, semipermeable membranes, perm tive membranes, etc.

Shrink Packaging.   The recent interest in shrink packaging lead one to believe that the process is relatively new. Actua French first used shrink packaging to preserve meats for the Line as far back as 1936. In 1948 the Cry-o-Vac process was comn introduced using a shrinkable polyvinylidene chloride copolyr Earlier yet, in 1926, cellulosic shrink bands were first introdu commercial use. These bands demonstrate a different shrink m from the usual heat activated shrinkage of most oriented ther films. Here, shrinkage of the film is caused by loss of water swollen regenerated cellulose bands. While heat increases t shrinkage, the same degree of shrinkage would eventually even at room temperature.

Bands are made in much the same way as cellophane. wood pulp is chemically dissolved to give a viscose so solution is subsequently extruded in tubular form into a bath. These tubes may be colored or printed or both. T moist until use and are shipped in the form of rolls or pre

Until recently, no competitive material had threatene for cellulosic bands. Now, heat shrinkable polyvinyl chloi range of diameters are becoming available. These can printed at least as easily as cellulosic bands and may wel

into the established markets for cellulosic bands. They have the advantage of not requiring special storage and handling conditions and can be supplied as rolls of colored, printed, flat tubing which is dry and readily adaptable to high speed machine application.

Both of these band materials suffer from one deficiency. Since they are supplied in tubular form and have to fit a diverse range of bottle diameters, it means that the manufacturer must inventory a large number of sizes, thicknesses, colors, etc. This portion of the packaging industry could be revolutionized and greatly simplified by the development of a heat shrinkable film which can be sealed to itself. This would mean that shrink bands could be made from wide rolls of film, printed and colored, then slit to the desired width. To date, the machinery has not been built to take advantage of this concept.

PLASTIC FILMS FOR SHRINK PACKAGING

It has long been known that almost any plastic which is stretched during its manufacture can be caused to shrink by reheating to its original stretch temperature. However, the widespread utility of this characteristic in plastic film was not appreciated until a few years ago. Today it has become apparent that shrink wrapping can cheaply do many packaging jobs which previously were difficult and often relatively expensive. As a result, a number of new or modified plastic films have recently been marketed with the sole objective of capturing a portion of the shrink wrap market. The ones currently commercial are listed in Table 8.1.

It is seen that a wide variation of properties is available. This is necessary for shrink packaging to grow. For instance, most cheese could not satisfactorily be wrapped in polyethylene films because good barrier properties are required of the wrap. Here, polyvinylidene chloride copolymers are required. At the opposite extreme, lettuce cannot be successfully shrink wrapped in saran type film because the barrier is too good. Oriented polystyrene seems to be the only film which has the required combination of gas and moisture vapor transmission rates needed to promote free breathing of the lettuce.

Most shrink wrap applications, however, are not as critical as the two foregoing examples and as a result several shrink films can adequately serve from a functional standpoint. Usually, then, a choice of film is made on a balance of film properties which includes price, appearance, ease of machinability, and other factors which may be more or less dominant for particular products.

TABLE 8.1.*   Properties of Shrink Films

Types of Shrinkable Films	Most popular Gauge (mils)	Cost 1,000 sq in. (cents)	Tensile Strength (psi)	WVTR (gm/mil)[2]	Oxygen Perm. (cc/mil)[3]	Maximum Shrink. %	Shrink Tension Range (lb/sq in.)[5]	Film Shrink Temp. Range (°F)[4]	Commercial Air Temp. Range (°F)[6]	Sealing Temp. (°F)
Polyester	.65	6.0	17–25,000	2.7–3.4	20–40	25–35	700–1,500	160–250	225–310	—
Polyethylene,[7] Type I	1.50	2.0	1,600–1,800	.8–9	10,000	15–40[8]	below 50	220–250	250–300	300–400
Crosslinked, Type I	1.0	3.5	8–13,000	.6–7	7,500	70–80	150–500	160–240	225–600	300–500
Crosslinked, Type II	.75	3.0	14–19,000	.3–4	3,500	70–80	250–1,000	200–280	260–600	300–500
Polypropylene	.50	2.5	15–27,000	.2–3	1,700	70–80	300–600	220–330	300–450	350–400
Polystyrene	1.0	2.3	9–12,000	4.0–9.0	3,500	40–60	100–600[9]	210–270	270–320	250–300
Polyvinyl chloride	.75	2.9	8–16,000[9]	3.3–14.0[9]	20–180[9]	50–70[9]	150–300[9]	150–300	225–310	275–345[9]
Polyvinylidene chloride copolymer	.60	4.0	6–20,000[9]	.2–1.4[9]	15–300	30–60[9]	50–150[9]	150–210	200–275	200–315[9]
Rubber hydro-chloride	.40	3.1	8–12,000	.9–1.4	3,000	40–50	150–350	150–230	225–300	180–250

* Reproduced by permission from *Modern Packaging Encyclopedia* for 1963. Copyright 1962 Packaging Catalog Corp., 770 Lexington Avenue, New York. Further reproduction prohibited.

[1] The reported data for gauge, cost, etc. are for the usual commercial grades, but the suppliers should be consulted for more complete information on other available gauges, types and the like. Also see film properties chart on p. 175 and listing for "Films, plastics, shrinkable" in the Buyers' Directory pages at the back of this book.

[2] ASTM—Method #E96–53T. Units = gm/100 sq in./24 hr/mil at 100°F at 90% RH.

[3] ASTM—Method #D1434–58. Units = cc/sq m/24 hr/mil at room temperature and 1 atmosphere.

[4] % Shrink (change from original) determined by five-second immersion of marked film sample in water for temperatures below 212°F or in silicone oil above 212°F. (Tests run in Cryovac laboratory.)

[5] Shrink tension determined by immersing film strip clamped in frame containing BLH Type SR⁴ Strain Gauge and reading maximum value. Hot water used below 212°F and silicone oil used above 212°F. (Tests run in Cryovac laboratory.)

[6] Higher temperature can be used to obtain faster shrink when accurately controlled. Great care is required (except for polyester and crosslinked polyethylene) since temperature is above the melting point.

[7] Type I is low density. Type II is medium density.

[8] Shrink is directional, varying from 15% maximum in the transverse direction to 40% in the longitudinal direction.

[9] Varies with film grade and method of manufacture.

In years to come, it appears inevitable that a greater variety of shrink films will become available to more precisely match film characteristics with package requirements. Thus, the trend that was started by cellophane to tailor-make films to suit specific package uses is expected to be extended to the shrink film area.

Advantages of Shrink Wrapping.   Shrink wrapping uses simpler, less costly equipment, which is at least as fast as conventional overwrap machinery. On this equipment many odd or irregular shaped items can be given a smooth contour wrap which has sparkling visibility and excellent protective characteristics. In many cases, there is no other way to do such a wrapping job (see Figure 8.1.).

The films which are used are without exception oriented by one of the techniques discussed in Chapter 2. Since oriented films may have up to 15 times the tensile strength of their nonoriented counterparts, on a weight for weight basis, the extra cost of orienting can be more than compensated for by the ability to use much thinner gauges to achieve a given package strength. This factor, in combination with relatively low cost automatic equipment, makes shrink wrapping economically attractive.

TECHNIQUES

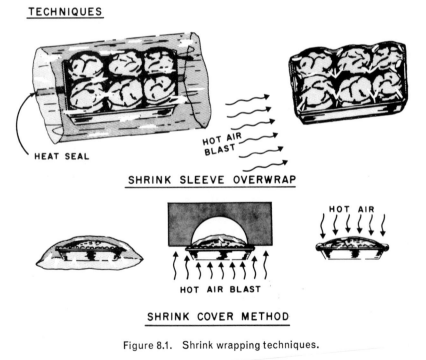

Figure 8.1.   Shrink wrapping techniques.

Techniques.   The techniques are limited only by the imagination of the user. Certainly a great number of novel package constructions will yet be developed in this field. A few of the common types in use today are:

(1) Shrinkable bags which may be filled, sealed, or clipped shut after air evacuation, then shrunk to fit the contours of the contents, e.g., polyvinylidene chloride poultry bags.

(2) Fruit tray overwraps which may be sleeves that are heat sealed on the bottom and then shrunk, or complete overwraps which are shrunk to immobilize tray contents.

(3) Tight fitting plastic covers may be shrunk on aluminum or even plastic trays by contour heating jigs.

(4) Protective produce wraps where, for instance, single heads of lettuce are hand wrapped in oriented polystyrene film, sealed on a hot plate, and passed through a heat tunnel.

Many variations can be carried out on these themes, and because of the wide variety of film properties already available, a much greater diversity of products can be shrink wrapped with cost savings than is currently being done.

The average shrinkage versus temperature behavior is illustrated in Figure 8.2 for the common types of shrink film. Available shrinkage is seen to vary from about 15–80%, depending on film type. A number of films are seen to have appreciable degrees of shrink at temperatures

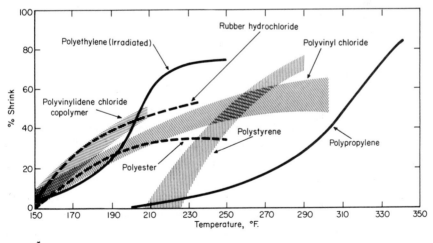

*Actual film temperature

Figure 8.2.   Shrinkage vs. film temperature.*

below 100°C. This allows the use of hot water as the heating medium. This can be an advantage since water has a high heat capacity, and, thus, will bring the film rapidly to its shrink temperatures. Other films, particularly polypropylene, require film temperatures of 150°C or higher to cause appreciable shrinkage. Here the shrink medium is necessarily limited to forced hot air.

All of these films become weaker at high temperatures, and it is important to carefully regulate the temperature of the shrinking medium to ensure that no portions of the film reach their melting points, or holes will result in the wrap. Overheating is least serious with the cross-linked polyethylenes that retain a higher percentage of their strength at elevated temperatures (they do not have a true melting point) than with any other of the films. However, appropriate temperature control will ensure satisfactory shrink wrapping with any of the shrink films.

Package design may also be critical, since some of these films exert shrink tensions in excess of 1,000 psi. This is sufficient to buckle a weak package.

Heat Shrinking Equipment.   The available units range from manual through semiautomatic to fully automatic, and each type has its place depending on the size of the operation, its location, etc. A typical unit is shown in Figure 8.3.

One very favorable factor for shrink wrapping is that prior wrapping operations can often be simplified when shrinkage is used as the final step to tighten the package. Shrink wrapping is certain to provide a growing outlet for oriented films in the years to come.

WATER-SOLUBLE FILM

A number of polymeric materials are water soluble and can be fabricated into water-soluble films. The chemical types currently in use or being actively evaluated are polyvinyl alcohol, polyethylene oxide, methyl cellulose, and carboxymethyl cellulose. Of these, the polyvinyl alcohol and polyethylene oxide appear most useful, since they are readily sealed and, in the lower molecular weight grades, have a high degree of water solubility. Solubility of these materials increases with temperature. Methyl cellulose, on the other hand, shows an inverted temperature–solubility relationship. That is, it is more soluble in cold water than in hot. Therefore, polyvinyl alcohol or polyethylene oxide is the preferred packaging material for bleaches, detergents, and blueing,

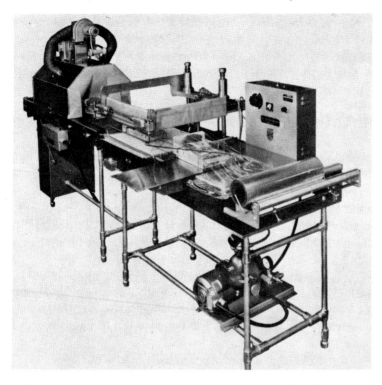

Figure 8.3. A semiautomatic shrink wrapping line. (*Courtesy of Great Lakes Stamp & Mfg. Co.*)

which are added to hot wash water, while methyl cellulose will probably find its main uses in prepackaging of food mix components which are used cold. Methyl cellulose has an advantage here in that it is completely nontoxic and is cleared for use as a food additive. Other items which have been prepackaged in polyvinyl alcohol film are insecticides and disinfectants.

Polyvinyl alcohol films also find use as mold release agents for pressure molding and vacuum bag molding, since the film is flexible, extensible, and does not adhere to most plastic materials. Solvent and oil resistant gaskets are also made from this material. Both methyl cellulose and polyvinyl alcohol have exceptionally good gas barrier properties when dry, but ways have so far not been discovered to utilize this property in packaging.

These films are generally fabricated into pouches and filled on form-fill-seal machines which have been modified to handle these water sensitive films. Because these films tend to embrittle when exposed to low humidity or to soften and tackify when exposed to high humidity, pouches are usually shipped in sealed polyethylene bags.

Indications are that as the technology for handling water soluble films is further developed, more uses will be found for this type of plastic film.

ARCHITECTURAL AND AGRICULTURAL USES FOR PLASTIC FILMS

In this area, established films are finding new uses, and new films are developing new applications.

Plastic Protective Coating. Outstanding among the newer films which are finding architectural uses is duPont's "Tedlar" polyvinyl fluoride film. This material has several outstanding properties which will help its acceptance in outdoor applications.

First, it is essentially transparent to the ultraviolet light found in solar radiation at sea level. This means that it degrades very slowly in comparison to almost any other plastic. Comparative weathering data is shown in Table 8.2. If this data is extrapolated, one could expect 15–30

TABLE 8.2.   Outdoor Weathering Life of Films*

Film	Thickness (mils)	Life[a] in Florida Test (Yr)
"Tedlar" PVF	2	7+
"Mylar" W	5	4
"Mylar" A	5	$\frac{1}{4}$
Copolyester laminating film	3	b
PVC (unplasticized)	5	$\frac{1}{2}$
Low density polyethylene	4	$\frac{1}{4}$
Cellulose acetate butyrate	5	$\frac{1}{2}$

* *Mod. Plastics* (July, 1959).

[a] Life values are the number of years' exposure required to decrease film elongation to 10%. Exposure samples were mounted unsupported (attached at edges only) on test racks facing south at 45% to the vertical.

[b] This film's elongation is only 4% before weathering.

years of service from a "Tedlar" film which is laminated to outdoor siding. Adhesive systems are available to bond "Tedlar" to aluminum, iron, plywood, masonite, etc., so that almost any facing material can be coated with this film. The initial cost of such a laminate is much higher than the cost of a coat of paint, but the fact that it remains maintenance free for many years can more than compensate for this factor.

The other properties which make "Tedlar" ideal for this application are:

(1) High strength (13,000 psi tensile at 28°C).

(2) Strength retention without embrittlement from below zero to above 180°C.

(3) Flexibility and fatigue resistance better than medium density polyethylene.

(4) Resists staining, chalking, abrasion, and permeation. Gas transmission rates are about the same as those of "Mylar".

In view of the outstanding combination of physical properties shown in Table 8.3, durability, ease of lamination, and colorability of this

TABLE 8.3. "Tedlar" Properties

	Type 20
Tensile strength 68°F	15,000 psi
300°F	3,300 psi
Elongation 68°F	100%
300°F	110%
Mullen burst	37 psi/mil
Flex life 0°F	40,000 cycles
68°F	70,000 cycles
Density	1.37 gm/cc
Tear strength	10 gm/mil
Impact strength	5 kg cm/mil

material, it appears inevitable that its use on various functional and decorative building panels will expand. At present there is no other plastic film available which can challenge the supremity of "Tedlar" at the same price level.

Glazing.   The other area that appears to hold a promising future for "Tedlar" is that of glazing. Again because of its toughness, temperature resistance, and transparency to ultraviolet radiation, this film is a natural for greenhouses. It may even be functionally superior to glass, since a greater proportion of the sun's radiation passes through this film than through glass.

Less expensive and less durable plastic films which are also finding some application in this area are 3–5 mil polyethylene, PVC, polyester, and 3–10 mil oriented styrene-acrylonitrile sheets. Even with the best of ultraviolet stabilizers, these films cannot be expected to last more than a few years.

Water Containment.   Relatively thin, 3–10 mil, black polyethylene is beginning to find a number of uses in water control applications. Usually, where irrigation of crops is required, water is expensive and it is uneconomical to allow large losses due to seepage into the soil from irrigation ditches and ponds. Under these conditions it has been found to be quite practical and economical to line ditches and ponds with black polyethylene film. Several years' durability is to be expected, since the film is not exposed directly to either sunlight or air. A secondary advantage is found here, since ditches and ponds so lined do not support vegetative growth and do not become clogged (see Figure 8.4).

Polyethylene film has been found effective from other standpoints, such as being an aid to strawberry culture. Plants are inserted through holes in the plastic film mulch, and the fruit that they bear never touches the soil, and thus remains very clean. The film also prevents moisture loss from the soil, increases the soil temperature, and promotes good root growth while preventing weeds from sprouting. Strawberry patches are notoriously difficult to cultivate once weeds get started.

Figure 8.4.   In Midland, Michigan, Dow's Well Department is installing a pond lined with polyethylene film each time it drills a new brine well. The film-lined ponds that it has already put in service now number thirteen. Each has a capacity of approximately 100,000 gallons. The film also has been used in Midland for the lining of a 1½ million gallon pond in which waste water is treated. (*Courtesy of The Dow Chemical Co.*)

To date, the economic advantage of a polyethylene mulch has only been proven for high value crops like strawberries, melons, pineapples, grapes, and tomatoes. However, a number of companies are actively investigating the use of plastic mulches on cotton and corn crops. Should the use of plastic film prove practical on such crops, a new market of up to 500 million pounds per year could develop. Since cost and not performance is holding back this large market, it seems likely that successful development of automatic machinery to simultaneously lay film, plant seeds, and fertilize them, will open up this market. Further, it appears that the film manufacturers will probably have to bear the cost of this development if it is to be widely adopted. Figure 8.5 illustrates an experimental mechanical mulching operation.

The need for this type of customer or application service work is equally plain in another agricultural opportunity for plastic films. It has been found that soil fumigation with gaseous or liquid herbicides, to rid it of insects, insect eggs, weeds, and disease organisms, increases the soil productivity tremendously. To do this practically and economically, machinery was developed which sprays the fumigant, lays the

Figure 8.5. Mulching with polyethylene film. Film edges are fed into trenches, then buried in a continuous operation. One man can handle the job with this experimental rig. (*Courtesy of The Dow Chemical Co.*)

film on top, and then seals it with soil on the edges. Here the film acts only as a gas barrier. After about eight hours the soil is sterilized and the film can be removed and either destroyed or reused.

A number of other agricultural applications which are just beginning to show promise are crop storage covers, tobacco seed bed covers, and plant covers for frost prevention after early planting and wind breaks.

Thinner grades of plain or colored polyethylene are beginning to be used extensively to aid in the curing of freshly poured concrete slabs and foundations. In order for concrete to cure to its optimum strength properties, it must be kept wet for several days. This is accomplished in a number of ways. It can be periodically sprayed, covered with wet straw or burlap or, easiest of all, simply covered with polyethylene. Since polyethylene is a good moisture barrier, the concrete that is cured under polyethylene, if reasonably well sealed, requires no attention at all until the curing is complete.

Vinyl films are being used as moisture vapor barriers beneath roofs, over foundations and around windows. The use of PVC film as a moisture barrier in shower stall construction is increasing as more municipal building codes approve this application.

Area Containment.   Here again polyethylene is finding widespread use as a wind and temperature screen. In skyscraper construction the skeletal steelwork is often completely encased in polyethylene to allow workmen to carry on under wind and weather conditions which would halt work in the absence of such an inexpensive weather barrier. These types of enclosures, in winter particularly, can often be heated sufficiently well to allow concrete to be cured even if the temperature outside is well below freezing (see Figure 8.6). Thus, this film has extended the number of working days per year for contractors in the less temperate climes and will likely continue to find greater use in these types of applications.

VACUUM METALLIZED FILMS

Metallized films are beginning to find the diversity of applications which metallized plastics, in general, have enjoyed for a number of years. These films have the appearance of thin metal foil but are tougher than foil and usually have a more highly reflective surface. Thus, metallizing gives all the appearance of highly polished metal plus the toughness of plastic films. The result is decorative, functional, less expensive, and more durable than the same article made from solid metal.

Figure 8.6.   Polyethylene film used as an inexpensive windbreak to allow construction to proceed in all but the coldest weather. (*Courtesy of The Dow Chemical Co.*)

This result is achieved by applying metal coatings up to 1/25,000 inch in thickness. Aluminum usually gives the most highly reflective surface, and it is the most common material used in this application. Other materials that have been used for different effects are gold, silver, tin, and zinc.

The application technique is based upon classical distillation theory. Any material which can be melted and caused to boil will exert a vapor pressure, and molecules of the substance will travel from the hot source to cool surfaces where they will condense. The evaporated molecules, like gas molecules, travel in straight lines until they collide with other molecules. Aluminum can be boiled at atmospheric pressure, but the distance travelled by evaporated aluminum molecules before encountering air molecules and being deflected from their straight path is very short. As the pressure is reduced, this straight line travel distance increases. It has been found that a pressure of .5 micron or less is required to obtain a long enough "mean free path" to make vacuum metallizing practical. This low air pressure is also required to prevent oxidation of the metals being vaporized. In operation, if the pressure is not sufficiently low, the evaporated coatings are dull instead of being highly reflective, due to oxide contamination in the metal.

As a result, most equipment developed to date for plastic film metallizing is of the batch type illustrated in Figures 8.7. and 8.8, where both unwind and rewind stations are enclosed within the vacuum chamber. Because of the very high vacuum requirements to obtain quality coatings, some films which contain either volatile plasticizers,

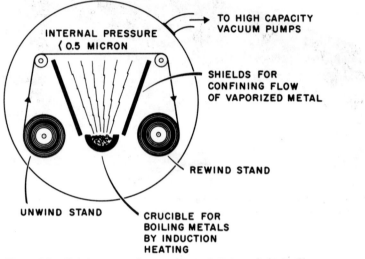

Figure 8.7.   Batch process for vacuum metallizing of plastic films.

Figure 8.8.   A batch style vacuum metallizer for plastic film being loaded prior to evacuation. Note the large vacuum pumps. (*Courtesy of NRC Equipment Corp.*)

water, residual solvents, or monomers often cannot be coated in this type of equipment. Examples of such films are cellophane, which contains water and glycol, or glycerol plasticizers and nylon, which may have absorbed considerable quantities of water. Even polystyrene films, which contain no plasticizers whatsoever, can cause problems if they contain even relatively low percentages of residual monomers, dimers, or trimers.

On thin films, the thickness of coating that can be applied may have to be considerably less than 1/25,000 inch, since the heat of condensation of thicker layers would cause film melting. At these thicknesses, the metal coatings appear continuous but are actually full of pinholes and may even be transparent to transmitted light to some degree. These coatings do decrease the permeability of the thin film but only by decreasing the area of film available for permeation. However, these films are sufficiently continuous to render the plastic surface conducting and, thus, free of static.

Little work has so far been done on metallizing with impure materials to obtain various levels of surface conductivity or even semiconducting properties, and this may be a fruitful area for future development work.

As the applications for metallized film continued to grow, more sophisticated continuous metallizers have been evolved. These are an order of magnitude more expensive than batch units but offer operating possibilities not attainable with the batch process. In these systems, demonstrated in Figure 8.9, film is fed from turret unwind stands through a series of chambers with ever decreasing pressure until they reach the metallizing chamber. Here they are coated and then pass through a similar set of exit zones of increasing pressure, and are

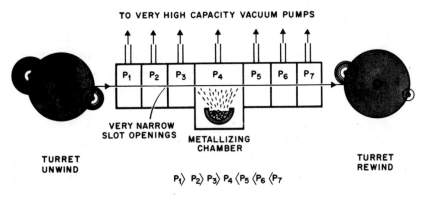

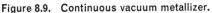

Figure 8.9.   Continuous vacuum metallizer.

rewound on a turret. These units can metallize high water content substrates such as paper because they effectively remove interfering vola-
tiles from the web before these reach the metallizing chamber. Thus,
now almost any web can be metallized if there is a market which can
justify the initial purchase of this sophisticated type of equipment.

Since freshly metallized surfaces are susceptible to oxidation, they
are often lacquered to maintain surface lustre. The use of tinted or dyed
lacquer sealing coatings often leads to spectacular decorative effects.

Table 8.4 summarizes the major current uses for vacuum metallized
films.

TABLE 8.4.   Uses for Metallized Plastic Films

Film	Metal	Application
Rigid PVC	Al	Synthetic Christmas trees; self extinguishing tinsel.
Polyvinylidene chloride	Al	Icicles for Christmas tree decorations.
Polyester	Al	Tinted and thin slit for blending in high fashion fabrics—i.e., Lurex.*
		Solar radiation reflectors, Echo satellites, labels, decorative decals, floor and wall tile additive when chopped fine, metallic ribbons.
Polystyrene	Al	Decorative wrapping.
Paper	Al	Decorative overwrap.
Cellulose acetate	Al	Vari-colored sequins, plain and fluorescent, labels, decorative trim on toys, furniture, automobiles and appliances.

Synthetic Fabrics made from Plastics Films.   Currently, two film
materials find usage in synthetic fabrics. These are polyester and polyvinylidene chloride.

The first is generally made from 50 gauge polyester film. This material
is vacuum metallized on one or both sides, then lacquered with a tinted
or clear coating to protect the aluminum deposit. After fabrication is
complete, this film construction is "fine-slit" into "monofilament"
which may be finer than $\frac{1}{64}$ inch. This fine slit film finds uses as an
additive to high fashion fabrics where some light reflectance is desired
to highlight the material. "Lurex"* is a typical example of this type of
material (see Figure 8.10).

The second, "Rovana"* is a rounded filament which is made from
narrow slit polyvinylidene chloride type film that has been oriented in
the machine direction only. This material is made from polyvinylidene
chloride latex which is converted to a nonoriented film. After fusing,

* Registered trade names.

Figure 8.10. This high fashion fabric uses white silk lace which is reembroidered with narrow ribbons of silver Lurex metallic yarn. (*Courtesy of The Dow Chemical Co.*)

this film is "fine-slit" and stretched to give a uniaxially oriented "monofilament" which can be handled on textile weaving machinery. This synthetic "fiber" features self extinguishing properties, strength, chemical and solvent resistance, and relatively low cost which make it suitable for such items as fireproof drapery, upholstery fabric, and filter cloth.

SEPARATION PROCESSES USING PLASTIC FILMS

Perm Selective Plastic Membranes. A process which may come to have the universal utility of distillation is the use of permselective membranes for the separation of mixtures of liquids or gases.

In some cases, this process may be thought of as being a filtration on a molecular scale. Here, the plastic film can be thought of as a barrier which is full of exceedingly small holes. For example, it has been calculated that polystyrene film could be used to separate helium from natural gas more cheaply than by using the liquefaction and distillation procedure. Figure 8.11 illustrates this principle.

The helium molecules are sufficiently small that they pass readily through the small pores in polystyrene film, while the methane and ethane molecules, which are considerably larger, pass through slowly and with difficulty. The net result is that the downstream gas composition is greatly enriched in helium content. When a second and third stage is added, nearly pure helium can, thus, be obtained.

A pilot unit* using fluorocarbon film has been evaluated for the separation of helium from natural gas. It has been proven less expensive than the quartz diffusion process but is still somewhat more expensive than the cryogenic process.

This perm selective membrane separation process has been considered to be completely dependent on molecular size of the permeants. In most cases, however, molecular size of the components of the mixture to be separated is only one of several factors which determine the relative rates of permeation. The most important of these are:

(1) Solubility of the permeants in the film material.

(2) Rate of diffusion of permeants dissolved in the film.

(3) Chemical and physical structure of the polymeric membrane.

Thus, acetone can be completely separated from chloroform using a "Teflon" polytetrafluoroethylene membrane, since it appears that chloroform forms a loose chemical complex with the film and cannot

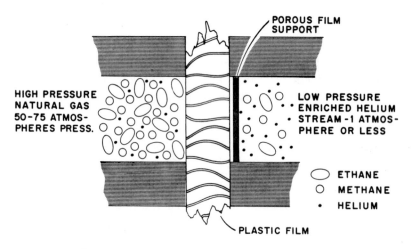

Figure 8.11.   Idealized selective permeation cell.

* *CEN*, p. 48 (April 29, 1963).

penetrate it, while acetone passes through without interaction. Another effect, that of solubility, becomes dominant in the separation of water from organic materials, such as ethanol, propanol, or methyl ethyl ketone, using cellulose acetate films. In this case, water is much more soluble in the film material than are the organic materials. Thus, it permeates much faster. Silicone films have been found to be as much as 1,000 times as permeable as polyethylene and quite selective as well. They may be used to extract air from sea water for undersurface dwellings.

Research and development on this novel separation process is still in its infancy, but it seems likely that when we learn how to tailor-make films with higher permeation rates and with selective behavior, sizeable amounts of plastic films will be used for this application. Naturally, these films will have to have long service life to be practical. Thus, it seems likely that the more chemical and oxidation resistant films such as polytetrafluoroethylene, irradiated polyethylene, polyester, and silicones will become of the greatest importance here.

Reverse Osmosis.   When an aqueous salt solution is separated from pure water by a membrane which is permeable to water but not to salt, water flows into the salt solution and exerts an osmotic pressure P_o. This process can be halted if the salt solution is contained under a hydraulic pressure P_n which exactly balances P_o. When P_n exceeds P_o, then water flows from the salt solution into the water (see Figure 8.12).

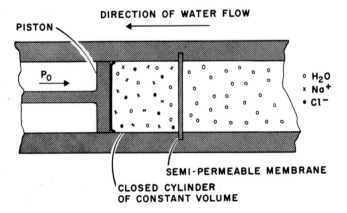

Figure 8.12.   Reverse osmosis cell. Direction of flow is reversed only when the pressure on salt solution exceeds P_o.

Thus, there are two obvious uses for this type of process.

(1) Concentration of inorganics in water solution.

(2) Separation of pure water from sea water.

The problems remaining before such processes can become economically practical are:

(1) Development of membranes with greater permeation rates.

(2) Design of equipment to utilize thin films at the necessary high pressures. For example, the osmotic pressure of the water-sea water system is 370 psi. To achieve high rates of separation using the reverse osmosis process, pressures well in excess of this must be utilized.

When these technical problems are solved, major quantities of plastic films, probably of the hydrophilic type (polyvinyl alcohol, cellulose acetate, nylon, etc.), could find utility in the process of separating water from brine.

A 300 gallon per day pilot plant using this principle was put into operation in 1964 by Havens Industries in San Diego. The membrane is treated cellulose acetate supported in porous fiberglass pipe. The plant runs at 800 psi pressure and in two passes, reduces the parts per million of salts from 35,000 to less than 200, which is well below the 500 parts per million acceptable in fresh water.

Plastic Foam Film and Sheet.   In the past, when demands for economies in plastics production were called for, it became customary to suggest adding air to reduce weight and, consequently, reduce unit costs. That some companies took this suggestion seriously is evidenced by the proliferation of producers of foam film and sheet. This material, made mainly of polystyrene, is available in thicknesses from 5 mils up and in densities as low as 2–5 lb per cubic foot. It can be made by either a tubular or a flat sheet process, where the extrudate foams as it leaves the die when the pressure on the blowing agent is relieved.

Because of its low density, such sheet can often compete economically with paper. This is the case with foamed meat trays and foamed apple trays. These compete quite successfully with the established pulpboard trays. Foam even has advantages, such as being sanitary, a good insulator, water insensitive, nonshredding, and capable of being molded into almost any desired shape. These properties combined with a low cost per unit area should lead to rather startling market growth for this material as soon as people learn how to use it and develop appropriate forming and handling machinery.

Summary. While sales of plastic films for packaging exceeded the one billion pound per year mark in 1964 and continue to grow at 6–8% per year, it is possible that the greatest growth potential in the future will be found in nonpackaging applications. The broader dissemination of knowledge of plastic film technology and properties should ensure a healthy future for the plastics film business.

Index

Index